EXERCISES IN ENGLISH

CO-AKB-052

Carolyn Marie Dimick

General Editor

Irene Theresa Kervick
Susan Mary Platt

Authors

OPTIMUS
MAGISTER
BONUS
LIBER

LOYOLA UNIVERSITY PRESS   CHICAGO

© 1989 Loyola University Press
3441 N. Ashland Ave.   Chicago, IL 60657
All rights reserved
Printed in the United States of America

ISBN 0-8294-0612-3

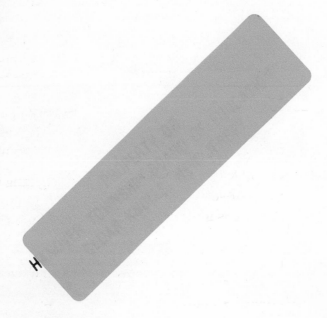

Table of Contents

Table of Contents

Recognition of Nouns

Exercise 1

A noun is a name word. A noun may name a person, a place, or a thing.

A. The following words are nouns. Rewrite each in the proper column.

	person	place	thing
1. skateboard			skateboard
2. rocket			rocket
3. daughter	doughter		
4. Canada		Canada	
5. player	player		
6. Disneyland		disneyland	
7. umpire	umpire		
8. Mexico		Mexico	
9. drums			drums
10. cheerleader	cheerleader		
11. boy	boy		

B. Underline the nouns in each sentence. The number of nouns is indicated in parentheses.

1. Each <u>month</u> has a special <u>jewel</u>, a special <u>flower</u>, and a special <u>color</u>. (4)

2. The <u>birthstone</u> is another <u>name</u> for the <u>jewel</u> of each <u>month</u>. (4)

3. The <u>flowers</u> for the <u>month</u> of <u>December</u> are the <u>poinsettia</u> and the <u>holly</u>. (5)

4. The <u>color</u> for <u>December</u> is red. (3)

5. The <u>color</u> and the <u>flowers</u> for the <u>month</u> of December make it a perfect <u>time</u> for <u>Christmas</u>. (6)

C. Complete each sentence with nouns.

1. My favorite foods are _pizzas_ and _tacos_ .

2. Some day I would like to visit _washington_ and _california_ .

3. My favorite holidays are _christmas_ and _Easter_ .

4. Wood can be used to make _fire_ and _houses_ .

5. When I grow up, I want to be a _docter_ or a _nurs_ .

Name

Proper and Common Nouns

Exercise 2

> There are two main kinds of nouns: proper nouns and common nouns.
> A proper noun names a particular person, place, or thing.
> A common noun names any one of a class of persons, places, or things.

A. Underline each proper noun. Circle each common noun.

1. Japan gave the United States cherry trees.

2. These trees were planted around the Tidal Basin in Washington.

3. Beautiful flowers bloom on these trees in April.

4. The blossoms are pink and white.

5. The flowers only last for ten or twelve days.

6. Photographers from many countries take pictures of the flowers.

7. The Jefferson Memorial is also decorated by these beautiful flowers.

8. In Japan, the people celebrate a festival when the buds appear.

9. Washington celebrates with a Cherry Blossom Festival.

10. America has received a beautiful gift from the country across the sea.

B. Write a proper noun for each common noun.

proper

1. candy bar _milkey way_

2. movie theater _Roxy_

3. cartoon character _mickey mouse_

4. brand of ice cream _Turkey hill_

5. basketball team _Sixers_

C. Complete each sentence with a proper noun to match the common noun.

1. My Uncle Mike bought a new _Van_ .
   (car)

2. Gerri shopped at _wise_ for the gift.
   (store)

3. _Disney world_ is where we went for our vacation.
   (place)

4. After the game, _Sandy_ treated us to a hamburger.
   (person)

2

More Proper and Common Nouns

Exercise 3

A. Write a common noun for each proper noun.

common   **common**

1. Canada — country   11. Boston —
2. Brian — *person*   12. Easter —
3. Florida — *State*   13. Sunday —
4. March — *month*   14. Alps —
5. Donald Duck — *Cartoon character* 15. Pacific Ocean —
6. North America — *Country* 16. Abraham Lincoln —
7. Thanksgiving — *Holliday* 17. Memorial Day —
8. Superdome — *Stadium*   18. Alexander Bell —
9. Atari — *game*   19. Buick —
10. Burger Bin — *food store* 20. Mississippi River —

B. Complete the sentence with proper nouns.

In ___*January*___, my family visited ___*Disney world*___
     (month)   (place)
and I saw ___*goofy*___.
          (person or thing)

C. Write a proper noun suggested by each common noun.

proper   **proper**

1. man — *Bill*   11. mountains —
2. country — *Mexico*   12. ocean —
3. singer — *Hilary Duff*   13. statue —
4. president — *Gorge Bush* 14. general —
5. astronaut — *Bob*   15. car —
6. holiday — *Christmas*   16. inventor —
7. comic strip —   17. street —
8. lake — *Erie*   18. store —
9. detective — *Relf Elf*   19. movie star —
10. seaport — *Boston*   20. restaurant —

Name

Singular and Plural Nouns

Exercise 4

A singular noun tells about one person, place, or thing.

A plural noun tells about more than one person, place, or thing.

A. Write **S** above the italicized word if it tells about one. Write **P** if it tells about more than one.

1. The potato *chip* (S) is an all-American *vegetable.* (S)

2. The *chips* (P) were introduced in a New York health *spa.* (S)

3. *Guests* (P) at the spa had had thin potato *fries* (P) in France.

4. An American *chef* (S) at the spa tried to copy the thin French *fries.* (P)

5. The *cook* (S) cut the *potatoes* (P) too thin for the fries.

6. These too-thin fried potatoes cooled and were called Saratoga *chips.* (P)

7. *People* (P) began nibbling this salty *snack* (S) and liked the *mistake.* (S)

8. The *chef* (S) was an American Indian *chief* (S) named George Crum.

9. Today *Americans* (P) eat about six hundred million *pounds* (P) of chips a *year.* (S)

10. The *recipe* (S) is so famous that it is in the White House *cookbook.* (S)

B. Complete each sentence with the plural or the singular of the noun.

pretzel *(pl.)* 1. _Pretzels_ were first baked by an Italian monk.

prayer *(pl.)* 2. Monks gave pretzels to children for learning their _prayers_

roll *(pl.)* 3. They took long thin _rolls_ of dough and folded them up.

arm *(pl.)* 4. The folds looked like children's folded _arms_ at prayer.

year *(pl.)* 5. For many _years_ the dough was baked soft like bread.

baker *(s.)* 6. A young _baker_ fell asleep while he was making them and they got very hard.

customer *(pl.)* 7. _Customers_ liked the hard crunchy pretzels.

shopkeeper *(pl.)* 8. _Shopkeepers_ discovered the hard pretzels stayed fresher.

treat *(pl.)* 9. These _treats_ can be made in your own kitchen.

factory *(s.)* 10. Julius Sturgis, a Pennsylvanian, opened the first pretzel _factorys_.

4

Writing Singular and Plural Nouns

Exercise 5

> Many nouns form the plural by adding *s* to the singular.
>
> Nouns ending in *s, x, z, ch,* and *sh* form the plural by adding *-es* to the singular.
>
> To form the plural of a noun ending in *y* with a consonant before it, change the *y* to *i* and add *-es*.
>
> To form the plural of a noun ending in *y* with a vowel before it, simply add *-s*.
>
> Some nouns ending in *f* (or *fe*) form the plural by changing the *f* (or *fe*) to *v* and adding *-es*.
>
> Some nouns form the plural by a change of vowels within the singular.
>
> Some nouns form the plural by adding *-en* or *-ren* to the singular.
>
> Some nouns have the same form in the plural as in the singular.

Read the letter and add plurals where needed.

Dear Mom and Dad,

I love visiting Uncle Ted on his farm. Yesterday we picked _peaches_ and
(peach)
cherries . At first, I wasn't a good picker. Uncle Ted told me that the
(cherry)
small field _mice_ would eat all the _berries_ that I dropped. They
(mouse)   (berry)
were so fresh that we didn't need _knives_ to get the _leaves_ off.
(knife)   (leaf)
Sometimes we only had to shake the _branches_ . The fruit was then
(branch)
packed in _boxes_ to be shipped to many _factories_ where it will
(box)   (factory)
be made into _jellies_ . We will have to look for the _jars_ on
(jelly)   (jar)
the supermarket _shelves_ .
(shelf)

Later in the week, Ned and I paddled our own _canoes_ on the lake.
(canoe)
It was so quiet that I saw many _deer_ with their _babies_ feeding
(deer)   (baby)
along the _shore_ . I thought that I would only see _herds_ of sheep
(shore)   (herd)
and _cow_ .
(cow)

This is a great vacation and I have taken many _pictures_ to share
(picture)
my _memorie_ with you.
(memory)

Your son,
Joey

Gender of Nouns

Exercise 6

> A noun has gender. The gender of a noun may be masculine, feminine, or neuter.
> The masculine gender indicates males.
> The feminine gender indicates females.
> The neuter gender indicates objects and places.
> Some nouns can be either masculine or feminine.

A. Write on the lines whether the italicized nouns in each sentence are
M—masculine, **F**—feminine, **N**—neuter, or **M/F**—masculine or feminine.

		F	M/F
1.	The little *girl* is afraid of the barking *dog*.	F	M/F
2.	The odd-looking *car* was a *Model T*.	N	N
3.	*Bill* left his hat on the school *bus*.	M	N
4.	*Maria* and *Rosa* painted the poster for the room.	F	F
5.	The *nurse* took the small boy's *temperature*.	M/F	N
6.	*Firefighters* raced into the burning *building*.	M/F	N
7.	*Fish* of all kinds were in his *tank*.	M/F	N
8.	The football *player* ran the length of the *field*.	M/F	N
9.	After the *game*, the *cheerleaders* were tired.	N	F
10.	*Barry* had books and *trophies* on his bookcase.	M	N

B. Write the feminine noun for each masculine noun.

	feminine			**feminine**
1. boy	girl	6. son-in-law	daughter-in-law
2. father	mother	7. bull	cow
3. uncle	Ant	8. gentleman	lady
4. rooster	Chicken	9. prince	Princess
5. doctor	nurse	10. king	Queen

C. Write eight neuter nouns found in your classroom.

1. Desk
2. Book
3. chair
4. pencil
5. Pencil shapener
6. black board
7. chalk
8. pen

Name

Nouns Used as Subjects

Exercise 7

> The case of a noun shows its relation to other words in the sentence.
>
> The person, place, or thing talked about in a sentence is the subject.
>
> A noun used as the subject is in the nominative case.

A. Underline the subject in each sentence.

1. Many tribes lived along the Atlantic coastline.

2. These Indians lived there long before Columbus.

3. Villages surrounded most lakes and rivers.

4. Six large tribes stretched from Canada to Florida.

5. A tribe was an independent nation.

6. The leader of a tribe was called a sachem.

7. The sachem inherited his role from his father.

8. A council of village leaders served with the chief.

9. The first colonists were helped by these Indians.

10. Chief Massasoit aided the Pilgrims.

B. Complete each sentence with a subject noun.

| sailor | hiker | diver | wolf | ballerina |
| child | wheel | students | athlete | dog |

1. The busy _students_ chattered quietly before the first class.

2. A lonely _wolf_ howled at the full moon.

3. The graceful _ballerina_ danced to the music.

4. That _sailor_ waved good-bye to his family.

5. The weary _hiker_ climbed slowly to the mountaintop.

6. A talented _athlete_ participated in the decathlon.

7. The curious _child_ peeked into the package.

8. The rusty _wheel_ squeaked loudly.

9. That _diver_ plunged perfectly into the pool.

10. An angry _dog_ growled at the mailman.

Nouns Used as Subjective Complements

Exercise 8

> A subjective complement completes the meaning of a linking verb and names the same person, place, or thing as the subject.
>
> A noun used as a subjective complement is in the nominative case.

A. Circle the linking verb in each sentence. Underline the subjective complement.

1. Snoopy (is) a black and white beagle.

2. Charlie Brown (is) the owner of Snoopy.

3. Woodstock (is) a small yellow bird.

4. Snoopy and Woodstock (are) friends.

5. Once Snoopy and Woodstock (were) hockey players on a frozen birdbath.

6. In the summer, the birdbath (is) a swimming pool for Woodstock.

7. Snoopy (is) a baseball player, too.

8. Charlie Brown (is) the manager of the baseball team.

9. The other players (are) friends of Charlie Brown.

10. Charles Schultz (is) the creator of all these characters.

B. Complete each sentence with a subjective complement.

1. A famous singer is _Lian Rrims_ .

2. In school, my favorite subject is _Spelling_ .

3. My teacher is _Jeanne_ .

4. The student across from me is _PJ_ .

5. In our school, the principal is _Phil_ .

C. Complete each sentence with the correct subjective complement.

~~Sunshine State~~   ~~Cornhusker State~~   ~~Lone Star State~~   ~~Golden State~~

1. California is the _Golden state_ .

2. Florida is the _Sunshine state_ .

3. Texas is the _Lone Star state_ .

4. Nebraska is the _Cornhusker State_ .

5. _Pennsylvania_ is the _Keystone Stat_ .
   (your state)

Nouns in Direct Address

Exercise 9

> When a noun is used in direct address, it names the person spoken to.
>
> A noun used in direct address is in the nominative case.

A. Underline the noun in direct address in each sentence.

1. <u>Folks,</u> step right up and get your tickets.

2. Be careful, <u>boys,</u> going down the steps.

3. These are box seats, <u>Dad!</u>

4. <u>Mr. Fox,</u> do you think we will be able to get autographs?

5. Maybe, <u>Jim,</u> we might get a few of them.

6. <u>Fans,</u> please stand for the national anthem.

7. Step up to the plate, <u>batter</u>.

8. I don't think that was a strike, <u>Dad!</u>

9. <u>Jim and Tod,</u> do you want a hot dog?

10. Do you want mustard, <u>boys,</u> on the hot dogs?

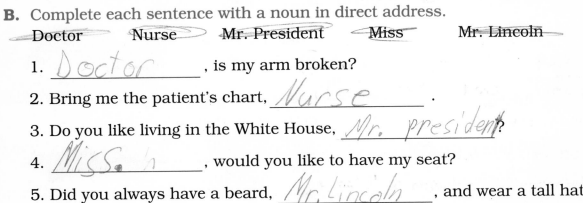

B. Complete each sentence with a noun in direct address.

Doctor   Nurse   Mr. President   Miss   Mr. Lincoln

1. _Doctor_ , is my arm broken?

2. Bring me the patient's chart, _Nurse_ .

3. Do you like living in the White House, _Mr. president_?

4. _Miss_ , would you like to have my seat?

5. Did you always have a beard, _Mr. Lincoln_ , and wear a tall hat?

C. Write sentences using each word as a noun in direct address. Vary the position of the noun.

José   1. _José, your up to bat._

Laura   2. _Laura, get me a diper._

class   3. _Class, get ready for a pop quiz._

Coach   4. _Coach, put me in._

swimmers 5. _Swimmers, get ready._

Nouns Used as Direct Objects

Exercise 10

The receiver of the action of the verb is the direct object. A noun used as the direct object in a sentence is in the objective case.

A. Circle the direct object in each sentence. Write on the line whether it answers the question *whom* or *what*.

what 1. During the American Revolution, Connecticut produced two famous men.

Whom 2. Connecticut claims Nathan Hale as a hero.

what 3. At first, Nathan Hale taught school.

what 4. Washington needed information about the British troops.

what 5. Hale joined the army of George Washington.

What 6. In his schoolmaster's clothes, Nathan crossed the British lines.

what 7. On the British side, Hale drew maps of the British troops.

what 8. He hid the maps and information in his shoes.

whom 9. Unfortunately, a British soldier recognized Hale.

whom 10. The British hanged Nathan Hale for spying.

B. Complete each sentence with a direct object.

battles   information   forts   town   mark
traitor   soldier   sides   hero   Benedict Arnold

1. Connecticut also produced a ___traitor___.

2. Americans remember ___Benedict Arnold___ as a spy.

3. American General Arnold planned ___battles___ with courage and skill.

4. But this traitor leaked ___information___ to the British.

5. Benedict Arnold changed ___sides___ during the war.

6. For the British, General Arnold captured two American ___forts___.

7. During battle, Arnold's troops killed every ___soldier___ in the fort.

8. His troops also burned the ___town___ of Griswald.

9. After the war, England accepted their ___hero___ as a citizen.

10. Nathan Hale and Benedict Arnold left their ___mark___ on history.

Nouns Used as Objects of Prepositions

Exercise 11

> The noun that follows a preposition in a prepositional phrase is called the object of the preposition. An object of the preposition is in the objective case.

A. Underline the prepositions in each sentence. Circle the object of each preposition.

1. The bat hangs head-downward in its cave.

2. The sharp claws on its toes cling to the cave's ceiling.

3. Bats sleep in this position.

4. At night, the bat awakes and flies out of the cave.

5. Its lips push into the shape of a horn.

6. Squeaking sounds come from its throat.

7. The noise vibrates the air in the cave.

8. The bat listens for echoes from its squeaks.

9. From its squeaks, the bat can "see" anything in the dark.

10. Bats are not blind in the day.

11. Bats are members of the mammal family.

B. Complete the paragraph with an object for each preposition in italics.

My friends dared me, so I walked *into* _____ . The insides were

covered *with* _____ . But I kept walking *up* _____ .

Soon my ears heard sounds *from* _____ . I felt a chill run

down _____ . I had a lump *in* _____ . My feet

were stuck *to* _____ . Suddenly, I felt a cold hand

on _____ . A cry finally came *from* _____ .

Turning around, I saw a man *with* _____ *in* _____ .

Can you finish the paragraph in one or two sentences?

_____

_____

_____

Possessive Forms of Nouns

Exercise 12

> The possessive form of a noun expresses possession or ownership. The apostrophe (') is the sign of a possessive noun.
>
> To form the singular possessive of a noun, add 's to the singular form of the noun.
>
> To form the possessive of plural nouns that end in s, add just the apostrophe to the plural of the noun.
>
> To form the possessive of plural nouns that do not end in s, add 's.

A. Write the singular possessive of each noun.

1. the whistle of the referee   the referee's whistle
2. the voice of the coach   *the coach's voice*
3. the horse of Paul Revere   *Paul River's horse*
4. the badge of the officer   *the officer's badge*
5. the spurs of the cowboy   *the cowboy's spurs*
6. the bark of the dog   *the dog's bark*

B. Write the plural possessive of each noun.

1. the cries of the babies   the babies' cries
2. the suggestions of both men   *the men's suggestion*
3. both wishbones of the turkeys   *both of the turkeys' wishbones*
4. the carts of the golfers   *the golfers' carts*
5. the tractors of the farmers   *the farmers' tractors*
6. the voices of the cheerleaders   *the cheerleaders' voices*

C. Underline the correct possessive form of the noun in each sentence.

1. The circus (<u>ringmaster's</u>, ringmasters') voice announced the next act.
2. The (<u>lion's</u>, lions') roar caused excitement.
3. Everyone laughed at the (clown's, clowns') trick car.
4. All of the (elephant's, <u>elephants'</u>) tails had pink bows on them.
5. All of the (child's, <u>children's</u>) eyes followed the tightrope walker.
6. One (<u>acrobat's</u>, acrobats') trick amazed everyone.
7. I liked how the (girl's, <u>girls'</u>) costumes glistened in the light.

Name _____

Review of the Possessive Forms

Exercise 13

A. Write the singular possessive and the plural possessive of each noun.

	singular possessive	plural possessive
1. doctor	doctor's	doctors'
2. baby	baby's	babies'
3. elf	elfs'	elves'
4. deer	deer's	deers'
5. nation	nation's	nations'
6. girl	girl's	girls'
7. wolf	wolf's	wolves'
8. child	child's	childrens'
9. fox	fox's	foxes'
10. army	army's	armies'

B. Complete each sentence with the correct possessive of the noun.

fox   1. The **fox's** tail was caught on a thorn.

nation   2. Our **nations** flag has changed many times.

doctor   3. Both **doctors'** reports showed the bone was broken.

baby   4. The **babies'** rattle was in the playpen.

man   5. The **man's** uniform is a shade of brown.

elf   6. Not one of the **elve's** coats fit properly.

deer   7. Walking in the forest, I saw a **deer's** white spots.

girl   8. All the **girls'** screams were loud and shrill.

wolf   9. In the evening, many **wolve's** cries fill the night.

child   10. At the park, the **child's** hot dog fell to the ground.

cow   11. The **cows** neck had a bell around it.

witch   12. The **witch's** power was known throughout the forest.

boy   13. I went to watch the **boys'** football game.

brother   14. My older **brothers'** rooms are never neat.

hen   15. My grandpa collects six **hens'** eggs every day.

13

Identifying Nouns

Exercise 14

Underline each noun. Above each noun write its use.

S—subject   **DO**—direct object   **OP**—object of preposition
SC—subjective complement   **DA**—direct address.

1. The duck quacked.

2. The balloon ascended into the sky.

3. Our frontier has vanished.

4. Marie forgot her umbrella at the zoo.

5. The chimes ring hourly.

6. The car skidded wildly.

7. The team won the game.

8. The captain praised the soldiers for their courage.

9. The sun melted the snow.

10. Marie unwrapped her gift at the party.

11. Joseph, empty the trash.

12. Thomas, recite your poem to the class.

13. That artist paints portraits of young children.

14. Thomas Edison was a famous inventor.

15. The friendly dog wagged its tail.

16. Firefighters rescued the family from the burning house.

17. Pilots face many dangers, class.

18. At the dance, David played the guitar.

19. My uncle is an electrician.

20. That gardener pruned the peach trees.

21. Uncle Eric was a fisherman.

22. Joan, pass the oatmeal cookies.

23. Portland is a beautiful city, Lillian.

24. That tall man is my brother.

25. Blanche, you have received an excellent report.

Name

Review of Nouns

Exercise 15

Write on the line whether the italicized noun is a person, place, or thing.

person   1. The French *people* gave America a gift in 1884.

thing   2. This gift was the *Statue of Liberty.*

thing   3. This *monument* was a sign of friendship and liberty.

person   4. *Édouard de Laboulaye,* a historian, suggested the idea.

place   5. The people of *France* donated money for the statue.

Write on the line whether the italicized noun is common or proper.

proper   6. *Frédéric Auguste Bartholdi* designed the statue.

common   7. The statue was to be built as a proud *woman.*

common   8. Her *crown* was made with seven spikes.

common   9. The spikes represented the world's seven seas and *continents.*

proper   10. She holds a book with the date of the *Declaration of Independence* on it.

Write on the line the gender and number of each italicized noun.

M—masculine   **F**—feminine   **N**—neuter   **S**—singular   **P**—plural

	gender	number
11. The *engineer* of the statue was Alexandre Gustave Eiffel.	M	S
12. Eiffel built the *skeleton* for the copper body.	N	S
13. *Sheets* of copper were hammered on the frame.	N	P
14. Bartholdi's *mother* was the model for the face.	M	S
15. These two *Frenchmen* shared their talents with America.	M	P.

Circle the subject in each sentence.

16. The (statue) stands 151 feet high.

17. The (base) of the statue rises 154 feet high.

18. The (height) of the monument is over 300 feet.

Circle the subjective complement in each sentence.

19. The crown of the statue is an (observation deck.)

20. Powerful lamps are the (lights) in the torch.

21. The home for this great lady is (New York Harbor.)

Review of Nouns

Exercise 15, continued

Circle the noun in direct address in each sentence.

22. (Momma,) look at the big statue!

23. Yes, (son,) she stands for freedom.

24. Soon we will be Americans, (children.)

Circle the object of the preposition in each sentence.

25. French workers built the entire statue in France.

26. Two hundred and fourteen cases carried the parts to America.

27. Frenchmen assembled the copper plates for the statue.

28. France presented the statue on July 4, 1884.

29. The dedication was made to President Grover Cleveland.

30. New York City celebrated with a grand parade.

Write on the line if the italicized noun is in the nominative or the objective case.

_____N_____ 31. Eiffel was a famous French *designer*.

_____ 32. ~~He designed the Eiffel Tower in *Paris*.~~

_____N_____ 33. The French *tower* stands 984 feet high.

_____N_____ 34. *Elevators* bring you to the top of the tower.

_____O_____ 35. Eiffel designed the huge *tower* for a World's Fair.

Complete the letter with the appropriate singular or plural form of each word. (36-45)

Dear Grandmom,

Our trip to New York City is great! A boat with _____benches_____ took us to
(bench)
the _____island_____. An elevator instead of all those _____stairs_____ sent us
(island)   (stair)
to the top. The crown is so high that all the small _____children_____ held on to an
(child)
_____adult_____. Looking out the _____window_____ in the _____crown_____,
(adult)   (window)   (crown)
you can see the harbor. There were _____visitors_____ from many
(visitor)
_____countrys_____. We are bringing you a special _____present_____.
(country)   (present)

Love,
Amy

Personal Pronouns

Exercise 16

> A personal pronoun takes the place of a noun. A personal pronoun is singular when it refers to one person or thing. A personal pronoun is plural if it refers to more than one person or thing.

A. Write on the line whether the italicized pronoun in each sentence is **S**—singular or **P**—plural.

_P_ 1. My parents gave *us* a surprise trip to Washington, D.C.

_P_ 2. *We* were going to see the nation's capital.

_S_ 3. *He* packed the car for the long trip.

_S_ 4. *She* studied the map for the correct routes.

_P_ 5. *They* wanted to go to the top of the Washington Monument.

_P_ 6. Dad went to the top with *them.*

_S_ 7. Jeff and *I* walked all the steps to the Lincoln Memorial.

_S_ 8. Joey asked *me* to hold his hand on the steps.

_P_ 9. Mom told *us* the story about the Vietnam Veterans' Memorial.

_S_ 10. Denise gave *her* a map of the Constitution Mall.

B. Write a pronoun that can take the place of the italicized words in the first sentence of each set.

1. *The Travers family* visited Washington, D.C. in the spring.

   They visited Washington, D.C. in the spring.

2. Jim and Jeff went to see the airplanes with *Mr. Travers.*

   Jim and Jeff went to see the airplanes with _him_ .

3. Denise and Joy showed Joey *the dinosaurs.*

   Denise and Joy showed Joey _it_ .

4. *Joy* loved the soda fountain in the History and Technology Building.

   She loved the soda fountain in the History and Technology Building.

5. Denise bought *the family* Washington, D.C. T-shirts.

   Denise bought _us_ Washington, D.C. T-shirts.

Three Kinds of Personal Pronouns

Exercise 17

> Personal pronouns name the speaker, the person spoken to, or the person spoken about.
>
> The personal pronouns that name the speaker are *I, me, we, us.*
>
> The personal pronoun that names the person spoken to is *you.*
>
> The personal pronouns that name the person or thing spoken about are *he, she, it, him, her,* and *them.*

A. Underline the personal pronouns that name the speaker.

1. Thoughtfully, I waited on the stage for the spelling bee to begin.

2. We were all a bit nervous.

3. During the contest, my teacher smiled encouragingly at me.

4. The judges gave us time to think.

5. I spelled the word very carefully.

B. Underline the personal pronouns that name the person spoken to.

1. Have you ever been in that position?

2. You should try facing an audience!

3. Looking at them, you can feel everyone is pulling for you.

4. Did you hear the word?

C. Underline the personal pronouns that name the person or thing spoken about.

1. Joe was so nervous; he laughed but spelled his word.

2. The crowd laughed with him.

3. After Joe, they all missed the same word.

4. Not one of them could spell the word.

5. Joe knew how to spell the word, and he won the contest.

D. Underline the pronouns in each sentence. Write on the line whether they are in the **1**— first person, **2**—second person, or **3**—third person.

_____3_____ 1. The judges gave him the prize.

_____1,2_____ 2. I want to thank you.

_____2_____ 3. You deserve this award.

_____1,1_____ 4. We can see that they all studied for this contest.

Recognition of Pronouns

Exercise 18

A. Circle the personal pronouns in each sentence. Write **1** above the pronouns that name the speaker. Write **2** above the pronouns that name the person spoken to. Write **3** above pronouns that name the person or thing spoken about.

1. We enjoyed the class picnic.
2. The dog followed me home.
3. Brent helped him.
4. They are friends from school.
5. It disappeared completely.
6. She is a sky diver.
7. The coach appointed me.
8. You wrote the best story.
9. We floated down the river.
10. She received a VCR for Christmas.
11. The company supplies them.
12. The team cheered them.
13. They found the treasure.
14. You answered my question.
15. It landed safely in the backyard.
16. We bought a new skateboard.
17. Handle it with great care.
18. The astronaut discovered it.
19. I found a five-dollar bill.
20. Will you help him and me?
21. She lost it in the lake.
22. They washed the car.
23. He helped her.
24. They treated us to ice cream.

B. Write sentences using a personal pronoun in the first person, second person, and third person.

first person   1. _____

_____

second person   2. _____

_____

third person   3. _____

_____

Name

Pronouns Used as Subjects

> A pronoun may be used as the subject in a sentence. Pronouns used as subjects are in the nominative case. The nominative case pronouns are *I, you, he, she, it, we, they.*

A. Circle the subject pronoun in each sentence. Write it on the line.

you   1. Do you know about Boys' Festival Day in Japan?

They   2. On that day, they fly a large 1600-pound kite.

_it_   3. It is a day everyone looks forward to.

they   4. They paint a fish on the kite.

_I_   5. I learned that the fish is a symbol for courage.

you   6. Do you know about Ben Franklin's kite?

_He_   7. He brought electricity out of the sky with the kite.

_he_   8. To tame that electricity, he invented the lightning rod.

_We_   9. We should be grateful to Ben Franklin.

_I_   10. I now know not to fly kites in a lightning storm.

B. Change the italicized word(s) in each sentence to a subject pronoun. Write the pronoun on the line.

_he_   1. *Eddie* watched the kite contest.

She   2. On this calm day, *Sis* was the only one to get her kite up.

She   3. *Jane* ran and ran with her kite.

_It_   4. On the grass, *the kite* lay lifeless.

They   5. *The kites* were on vacation.

C. Complete each sentence with a subject pronoun. Vary your choices.

1. On windy days, ___they___ rise quickly.

2. ___We___ have trouble holding the kite line.

3. Have ___you___ ever lost a kite?

4. ___he___ chased one kite for blocks and blocks.

5. Some kites ___We___ will never find.

Name

Pronouns Used as Subjective Complements

Exercise 20

> A pronoun may be used as the subjective complement in a sentence. Pronouns used as subjective complements are in the nominative case.

A. Circle the correct subject pronoun. Write the sentence in reverse to show that the subjective complement can be used as the subject.

1. The builders of the ships are (**they**, them).

_____

2. The happiest boys after the game were (us, **we**).

_____

3. The writer of the winning composition is (**he**, him).

_____

4. The Halloween goblin was (**I**, me).

_____

5. The singers in the show are (them, **they**).

_____

6. The actress from the television show is (her, **she**).

_____

7. The cook in Helen's kitchen is (**she**, her).

_____

8. The first volunteers for the job were (them, **they**).

_____

B. Complete each sentence with a subjective complement. Vary your choices.

1. The pitcher for the New York Yankees is ___she___ .

2. Is that ___he___ ?

3. The most faithful nurse is ___she___ .

4. This is ___I___ .

5. The sick boy is ___he___ .

6. The new teachers are ___they___ .

7. It was ___she___ .

Writing Subjective Complements

Exercise 21

A. Underline the subjective complement(s) in each sentence. Write on the line a subject pronoun to take the place of the subjective complement(s).

_____ 1. That boy is Brian.

_____ 2. It is grandfather.

_____ 3. The girl near the desk is Betty.

_____ 4. The dancers are Linda and Molly.

_____ 5. The writer of the paragraph is Andy.

_____ 6. The woman in the store is Ginny.

_____ 7. Is that Todd?

_____ 8. The best driver is Philip.

_____ 9. The mowers were Joe and Ed.

_____ 10. The boy on the bike is my brother.

B. Complete each sentence with the correct subjective complement.

1. Was that _____ ? *(third, singular, fem.)*

2. No, it was _____ . *(third, singular, masc.)*

3. The farmer was _____ . *(third, singular, fem.)*

4. The best painters were _____ . *(third, plural, masc. or fem.)*

5. The person in the last desk is _____ . *(first, singular, masc. or fem.)*

6. Who is knocking? It is _____ . *(second, singular, masc. or fem.)*

7. The owners of the dog were _____ . *(first, plural, masc. or fem.)*

8. Was it _____ who asked the question? *(second, singular, masc. or fem.)*

9. Yes, it was _____ . *(first, singular, masc. or fem.)*

10. The president of the club is _____ . *(third, singular, masc.)*

Pronouns Used as Direct Objects

Exercise 22

> A pronoun may be used as the direct object in a sentence. Pronouns used as direct objects are in the objective case. The object pronouns are *me, you, him, her, it, us, them.*

A. Write on the line an object pronoun to take the place of the italicized words in each sentence.

_____ 1. The Soap Box Derby races *motorless cars.*

_____ 2. Foxy built *a small wooden box* with wheels.

_____ 3. Beany helped *Foxy* with the design.

_____ 4. Uncle Frankie examined *the model* daily.

_____ 5. Aunt Dottie encouraged *Foxy and Beany.*

_____ 6. Finally the two friends finished *the project.*

_____ 7. At the race, the officials checked *the driver.*

_____ 8. A foxtail on the back of the car puzzled *the judges.*

_____ 9. During the race, the foxtail held *the lead.*

_____ 10. Victoriously, the soap box crossed *the finish line.*

B. Complete each sentence with an object pronoun.

1. The judges gave _____ a grand trophy.

2. They held _____ high in the air.

3. The reporters wanted _____ to say a few words.

4. Aunt Dottie treated _____ after the race.

5. Foxy thanked _____ for the design.

C. Underline the object pronoun in each sentence.

1. Proudly Foxy carried it home.

2. The neighbors met them there.

3. Uncle Frankie praised them for their work.

4. The family wanted them to pose for more pictures.

5. A strong wind pushed it to fame.

Pronouns Used as Objects of Prepositions

Exercise 23

> A pronoun may be used as the object of a preposition in a sentence. Pronouns used as objects of prepositions are in the objective case.

A. Circle the preposition in each sentence. Write on the line the object pronoun to take the place of the italicized words.

_____ 1. For *Brian*, class picture day was exciting!

_____ 2. The photographer gave directions to *the class*.

_____ 3. Then Mr. Ansel looked into *the lens*.

_____ 4. Next he glanced at *the flowering trees*.

_____ 5. The location near *the trees* was perfect!

_____ 6. The class moved across *the lawn*.

_____ 7. Again the photographer looked at *the boys and girls*.

_____ 8. Now Mr. Ansel motioned toward *the last girl*.

B. Follow these directions for the next exercise.

1. Put your name on blanks 5 and 10 before the slashes.
2. Put your friends' names on all other blanks before the slashes.
3. Substitute pronouns for all the objects of the prepositions.
4. Write these object pronouns on the blanks after the slashes.
5. Read the paragraph with the pronouns in place and answer the last question.

At the Magic Laser Contest, we put a quarter in the machine. Suddenly a

purple laser beam flashed around (1) _____/_____ , over

(2) _____ /_____ , between (3) _____ and

(4) _____/_____ . It bounced off (5)_____ /

_____ and came right at (6)_____/_____ . Ducking, I saw

it whiz by (7) _____ /_____ , who was beside

(8) _____ /_____ . Unexpectedly, the beam moved toward

(9) _____ /_____ , but at the last second, the beam zoomed

through (10) _____ /_____ .

Who got zapped? _____

Use of Pronouns: *I* and *Me, We* and *Us*

Exercise 24

I and *we* are nominative case pronouns.

Me and *us* are objective case pronouns.

A. Complete each sentence with the pronoun *I* or *me.*

1. _____ raked the leaves into a pile.

2. Take _____ with you.

3. That was _____ .

4. _____ have finished the work.

5. A little dog chased _____ .

6. _____ like fresh strawberries.

7. Shaw will take _____ to the game.

8. _____ cleaned the fishing poles.

9. The boy at the microphone was _____ .

10. _____ ate the whole bowl of soup.

B. Complete each sentence with the pronoun *we* or *us.*

1. _____ scattered popcorn for the birds.

2. _____ picked fresh berries.

3. Did the dentist call _____ ?

4. _____ must hurry.

5. The news amazed _____ .

6. May _____ sing the new song?

7. Please take _____ to the movie.

8. _____ have lost our way.

9. Can you give _____ a ride home?

10. _____ reached the house quickly.

11. The letter was sent to _____ .

12. _____ rode our bikes all day.

Name

He and *Him*, *She* and *Her*, *They* and *Them*

Exercise 25

He, she, and *they* are nominative case pronouns. *Him, her,* and *them* are objective case pronouns.

A. Cross out the incorrect pronoun in parentheses.

1. (They, Them) are the men working on the car.

2. A bee stung (him, he) on his hand.

3. Has (he, him) found the bat and ball?

4. (She, Her) has fallen into the mud.

5. The directions puzzled (she, her).

6. (She, Her) has bright-colored clothes and pretty jewelry.

7. (He, Him) broke all the dishes by accident.

8. Mrs. Kervick rewarded (him, he) with two goldfish.

9. Have you met (they, them)?

10. (He, Him) beat the big Texas Longhorn drum in the parade.

B. Complete each sentence with the correct pronoun.

he/him	1. Is that _____?
they/them	2. The baby followed _____ into the next room.
They/Them	3. _____ built the fire for the cookout.
she/her	4. That was _____.
He/Him	5. _____ spread mustard on the pretzel.
He/Him	6. _____ is the nearest boy to the window.
she/her	7. Nora wants _____ to dance.
They/Them	8. _____ planned the party for the birthday.
he/him	9. His little brother obeyed _____.
He/Him	10. _____ won the regional swim meet.
she/her	11. Nora told _____ the news.
they/them	12. Their teacher asked _____ to write a song.

Review of Subject and Object Pronouns

Exercise 26

> The subject pronouns are *I, you, he, she, it, we, they.*
> The object pronouns are *me, you, him, her, it, us, them.*

A. Underline the personal pronouns in each sentence. Write **N** on the line if they are in the nominative case. Write **O** on the line if they are in the objective case

1. She covered them with dirt and leaves. _____ _____

2. It destroyed them in a few seconds. _____ _____

3. She brings the mail to us each day. _____ _____

4. Has he prepared the dinner for you? _____ _____

5. It was I who told Amanda the funny story. _____ _____

6. The teacher selected him and me. _____ _____

7. Meet her at the park for me. _____ _____

8. It was you. _____ _____

9. You should collect the papers for him. _____ _____

10. I left the building with you, Chuck. _____ _____

B. Circle the correct pronoun in parentheses.

1. (We, Us) own three pets: a dog, a cat, and a mouse.

2. The barking dog frightened (me, he).

3. (Me, I) heard the whistle on the freight train.

4. The best person for the job is (she, her).

5. Keith bought (they, them) a trick pencil.

6. (She, Her) likes to munch on salty pretzels.

7. Teddy put the puzzle together for (him, he).

8. (Them, They) beat the drums with drumsticks.

9. Have (you, us) read the poem about talking potatoes?

10. Agnes gave (we, us) scratch-and-sniff stickers.

Possessive Pronouns

Exercise 27

Possessive pronouns show possession or ownership by the speaker, the person spoken to, or the person or thing spoken about. The possessive pronouns are *mine, yours, his, hers, its, ours, yours, theirs.*

Note how possessive pronouns can take the place of possessive nouns.
The skateboard is Cole's.   The skateboard is **his**.

A. Underline the possessive pronoun in each sentence.

1. Is that yours?

2. Hers is on the desk in the second aisle.

3. Is that ten-speed bike yours?

4. The best work on the bulletin board is his.

5. The shiny red sports car is ours.

6. Where is hers?

7. Mine is in the back of the closet.

8. The small black and white puppy is hers.

9. Yours is older than mine.

10. The idea was his.

B. Write on the line a possessive pronoun to replace the italicized words.

_____ 1. That tall black hat is *Lincoln's.*

_____ 2. I lost my book but I found *Lisa's and Jan's.*

_____ 3. My hit was a double but *Jason's* was a homer.

_____ 4. *Julie's book* is the lost one.

_____ 5. *Mr. Pell's and my tomatoes* are the biggest and reddest.

_____ 6. Did you ask your teacher about *my books?*

_____ 7. *Your coat* is on the hook in the closet.

_____ 8. My dog is bigger than *Vanessa's.*

_____ 9. Do you care if I use your bat or *Don's?*

_____ 10. *Mom's and Dad's rings* are made of pure gold.

Pronouns in Contractions

Exercise 28

Some personal pronouns are used with verbs to form contractions. A contraction is a word made by joining two words.

The apostrophe (') is used to show the missing letter or letters in a contraction.

A. In the paragraph, make each set of words in parentheses a contraction. Write the contraction on the line.

My name is Harry Hardner and (I have) _____ a very strange baseball story.

(I will) _____ begin by telling you that baseball fields didn't always have fences.

So, no matter how far you hit the ball, (it is) _____ still in play. In this

particular game, (we are) _____ up to bat and I really hit the ball.

(They are) _____ still talking about how far it went. Excitedly, (I am) _____

running around the bases and heading for home. But my team is shouting,

"(You are) _____ to go back to first base!" (I am) _____ surprised to find

out that I didn't tag that base. "Hurry or (he will) _____ tag you out!"

(I would) _____ have to go back to first base or be out. I just got there as the

ball came in but I heard the ump say, "(You are) _____ safe!"

"(I will) _____ only get a single?" I asked the ump. "(They are) _____ the

rules," he answered. "(It is) _____ not fair!" shouted my teammates. Later my

teammates tried to make me feel better by telling me, "(You are) _____ the only

person to have a five-base hit and no runs."

B. Write sentences using the following words as contractions.

she will   1. _____

I will   2. _____

we have   3. _____

they are   4. _____

it is   5. _____

you will   6. _____

we are   7. _____

I am   8. _____

Name

Compound Personal Pronouns

A compound personal pronoun ends in *-self* or *-selves*.

singular	**plural**
myself	ourselves
yourself	yourselves
himself, herself,	themselves
itself	

A. Underline the compound personal pronoun in each sentence.

1. At the school play, I saw him myself.

2. The postman himself brought the package to the door.

3. The empty cabinet itself is very heavy.

4. Did you check the answer yourself?

5. Mr. Davis closed the doors himself.

6. The girls amused themselves with the sticker book.

7. He blamed nobody but himself for the accident.

8. Prepare yourself for the safe-skateboard examination.

9. I myself find history very interesting.

10. Suddenly I found myself lost in the woods.

B. Complete each sentence with the correct compound personal pronoun.

1. They helped _____ to the birthday cake.

2. Tina _____ did the report on tropical storms.

3. A selfish person thinks only of _____.

4. The boys _____ designed the model Civil War battlefield.

5. The test _____ wasn't too difficult.

6. The crowd exhausted_____ cheering during the game.

7. I laughed at_____ for being so ridiculous.

8. We _____ organized the school fair.

9. The guitarist _____ entertained the crowd.

10. What action did you _____ take?

Review of Pronouns

Exercise 30

Write on the line whether the italicized pronoun is
1—the speaker, **2**—the person spoken to, or **3**—the person spoken about.

_____ 1. Mr. Secretary, *I* need wagons for the supplies.

_____ 2. But Miss Barton, *we* don't have horses for the wagons.

_____ 3. *You* can't allow the men to be without these things.

_____ 4. *They* need medical supplies badly.

_____ 5. *You* are a brave woman.

_____ 6. Mr. Stanton, allow *me* to go to the battlefield.

_____ 7. That is where *I* am needed most.

_____ 8. The wounded require attention before *they* are moved.

_____ 9. Nursing *them* out there is necessary.

_____ 10. But *you* could get hurt on the battlefield.

Circle the compound personal pronoun in each sentence.

11. She herself was called the "Angel of the Battlefield."

12. "Clara, prepare yourself for the worst," the officers warned.

13. The men helped themselves the best they could.

14. I myself could never do what Clara did.

15. The work itself was difficult, but Clara was determined.

On the line, write **S** if the italicized pronoun is the subject. Write **SC** if it is the subjective complement.

_____ 16. Our swimming teacher is *she.*

_____ 17. *She* taught my brother Chris.

_____ 18. The lifeguard is *he.*

_____ 19. At the pool, *he* got his swimming badge.

_____ 20. *He* takes his responsibility seriously.

Review of Pronouns

Exercise 30, continued

On the line, write **DO** if the italicized pronoun is the direct object. Write **OP** if it is the object of a preposition.

_____ 21. Near *me,* a small child jumped into the pool.

_____ 22. The little girl called *them.*

_____ 23. The water was too deep for *her.*

_____ 24. I reached *her* quickly.

_____ 25. The mother thanked *me* afterwards.

Write the correct pronoun on the line.

she/her   26. The Red Cross will give _____ swimming lessons.

They/Them   27. _____ help swimmers learn safety in the water.

we/us   28. Instructors taught _____ all the rules for safety.

me/I   29. Mr. Burroughs, _____ think I am ready to begin.

them/they   30. Lessons prevent _____ from having accidents.

Write on the line a possessive pronoun for the italicized words in each sentence.

_____ 31. The high white chair with the umbrella is *the lifeguard's.*

_____ 32. *Alison's whistle* is around her neck.

_____ 33. Where is *your whistle?*

_____ 34. *My water aerobics class* begins on Tuesday.

_____ 35. *Keith's and my lifesaving classes* are just about over.

Write on the line the contraction for the words.

36. I will   _____

37. you are   _____

38. it is   _____

39. I would   _____

40. we have   _____

Name _____

Descriptive Adjectives

Exercise 31

| A descriptive adjective describes a noun or a pronoun. |

A. Underline the descriptive adjectives in each sentence. The number in parentheses tells how many descriptive adjectives are in each sentence.

1. The Olympics bring together the finest athletes. (1)

2. Colorful ceremonies open this world event (2)

3. A dramatic moment in the opening is the lighting of the flame. (1)

4. Cross-country runners relay a lighted torch to the crowded stadium. (3)

5. The torch is brought from the historic site of the ancient games. (2)

6. The official flag is raised while blazing trumpets blare. (2)

7. A peace symbol of white doves flood the skies. (2)

8. A spectacular parade of the competing athletes follows. (2)

9. Cheering fans enjoy this impressive ceremony. (2)

B. Complete each sentence with a descriptive adjective.

excited	nervous	powdered	powerful	nimble
tired	lean	exhausted	confident	graceful
agile	happy	shaking	trembling	joyful

1. The female gymnast performed _____graceful_____ floor exercises.

2. _____ muscles are needed for the wooden rings.

3. On the balance beam, the athlete's _____ feet moved swiftly.

4. The_____ cyclist pumped the pedals of the fifteen-speed bike.

5. The _____ hands of the small gymnast reached for the uneven parallel bars.

6. The _____ pole vaulter looked anxiously at his opponent.

7. In the water, the_____ swimmer gasped for air.

8. On the diving board, the_____ diver awaited the starting signal.

9. Tying his shoes, the _____ sprinter looked down the course.

10. The_____ hockey team hugged their tearful coach.

C. Circle the descriptive adjectives that were already in exercise B.

Proper Adjectives

Exercise 32

> Proper adjectives come from proper nouns. These descriptive adjectives begin with a capital letter.

A. Underline the proper adjective in each sentence.

1. Ancient Olympic games were religious festivals.

2. The Roman soldiers changed the festivals to contests.

3. The games disappeared from Western culture for fifteen hundred years.

4. A group of German archaeologists found the ruins in 1875.

5. A French educator organized the modern competition.

6. The Greek people hosted the first modern games.

7. The Winter Games have been hosted by the Canadian nation because of the snow.

8. Recently, the Summer Games were hosted by the Korean nation.

9. The Scandinavian nations have talented athletes for the Winter Games.

10. American athletes make us proud of both Winter and Summer Games.

B. Complete each sentence with the adjective formed from the proper noun at the left.

America   1. The _____ diver scored a perfect ten.

Poland   2. Breaking a record, the _____ runner finished the marathon.

Russia   3. Dancing her way to fame, the _____ skater performed beautifully.

Cuba   4. The _____ players scored the winning point.

France   5. The _____ cyclists pedaled to the top of the Velodrome.

Italy   6. One of the _____ relay runners dropped the baton.

Ireland   7. The _____ long-distance runner trained in America.

China   8. In the floor exercise, the _____ gymnast performed to modern music.

Japan   9. Even in a blinding snowstorm, the _____ ski jumper out-distanced everyone.

Canada 10. The _____ basketball team lost by only one point.

Name _____

Limiting Adjectives; Definite and Indefinite Articles

Exercise 33

A limiting adjective points out an object or tells how many.

The articles are *the*, *a*, and *an*. *The* is a definite article. *A* and *an* are indefinite articles. *A* is used before words beginning with a consonant sound. *An* is used before words beginning with a vowel sound.

A. Complete each sentence with the definite article *the* or an indefinite article *a* or *an*.

1. Gymnastics is _____ sport in which contestants perform acrobatic exercises.

2. Two or more teams compete at _____ gymnastic meet.

3. _____ gymnastic meet has six events in _____ contest.

4. _____ gymnast's performance is called _____ routine.

5. Anyone who performs in all six events is called _____ all-around gymnast.

6. They must also perform _____ optional routine.

7. In the floor exercise, _____ routine must be a constant series of movements.

8. _____ floor routine is always done to music.

9. Other exercises are _____ pommel horse, _____ horse vault, _____ rings, _____ parallel bars, and _____ horizontal bars.

10. Scores are given by _____ judges who watch _____ exercises.

B. Complete each set of words with *a* or *an*. Then complete each sentence.

1. __An__ athlete _____must train for his sport._____

2. _____ automobile _____

3. _____ baton _____

4. _____ oval track _____

5. _____ relay race _____

6. _____ sprinter _____

7. _____ official's gun _____

8. _____ false start _____

9. _____ eight-lane track _____

10. _____ runner _____

11. _____ uneven starting line _____

35

Demonstrative Adjectives

Exercise 34

> The demonstrative adjectives are *this*, *that*, *these*, and *those*.
>
> *This* and *that* point out one person, place, or thing.
>
> *These* and *those* point out more than one person, place, or thing.
>
> *This* and *these* name persons, places, or things that are near.
>
> *That* and *those* name persons, places, or things that are far.

A. Circle the correct demonstrative adjective in parentheses.

1. In pair skating, (this, these) two compete regularly.

2. (That, Those) skating outfit is a beautiful color.

3. The sequins on (that, those) blouses glitter in the lights.

4. Having matching outfits makes (that, those) pair look stylish.

5. (This, These) pair of skates match the sequined outfit perfectly.

6. For jumps on the ice, (these, this) skates have toe picks.

7. (That, Those) couple on the ice does ice dancing.

8. In their routine, (that, those) skaters can't do lifts.

9. Fast-moving music keeps (this, these) two skating quickly.

10. (This, These) type of skating looks like ballroom dancing.

11. The winner receives (this, these) medal.

B. Complete each sentence with the correct demonstrative adjective.

1. Figure skaters use _____ *(near)* type of skate.

2. _____ *(near)* skates have teeth cut in the front blade.

3. Spins and figures are made with _____ *(near)* toe rakes.

4. The bottom of _____ *(near)* skates is also curved.

5. _____ *(far)* skate is used just for ice racing.

6. _____ *(far)* skate boots are low-cut and lightweight.

7. Steel tubing reinforces _____ *(far)* thin, flat blades.

8. The blade and boot on _____ *(far)* skates are designed for speed.

9. _____ *(near)* ice-hockey skates have a very heavy boot.

10. Players get support and protection from _____ *(far)* shoe.

Possessive Adjectives

Exercise 35

> A possessive adjective shows ownership.
>
> The possessive adjectives are *my, your, his, hers, its* in the singular and *our, your, their* in the plural.
>
> A contraction is made from two words. A contraction uses an apostrophe. Note the difference between possessive adjectives and contractions.
>
> | possessive adjective | contraction |
> | --- | --- |
> | its | it's—it is |
> | your | you're—you are |
> | their | they're—they are |

A. Underline the possessive adjective in each sentence.

1. Our class had its own Olympics.

2. Everyone kept his own score.

3. The events tested your silliness.

4. We paddled our skateboards with plungers.

5. I had trouble keeping my feet on the skateboard.

6. Walking a floor balance beam, Tina kept the book on her head.

7. Debbie leaned her forehead on the upright bat and walked around it.

8. Afterwards she had trouble with her balance.

9. How high can you count with a pencil between your nose and top lip?

10. The boys were able to hold more pencils behind their ears than the girls.

B. Circle the correct word in parentheses.

1. (Their, They're) reasons for not winning were many.

2. The stick and (its, it's) plunger did not stay together.

3. (Your, You're) sure they didn't use glue?

4. (They're, Their) lips were certainly sticky!

5. (Your, You're) ears are bigger than mine.

6. (Its, It's) not my fault that my feet come in that size!

7. (Their, They're) dizzy from walking around a bat.

8. (Its, It's) because my head is so round that the book fell.

9. You won because (your, you're) lips are better than mine!

10. This was not (your, you're) typical athletic contest.

More Limiting Adjectives

Exercise 36

> Some limiting adjectives tell how many.
>
> A number can be a limiting adjective—*one, two, three*
>
> A word telling about a number order can be a limiting adjective—*first, second.*
>
> The following words can also be limiting adjectives.
>
> | | | | | |
> |---|---|---|---|---|
> | *all* | *both* | *few* | *neither* | *every* |
> | *another* | *each* | *many* | *some* | *much* |
> | *any* | *either* | *most* | *several* | |

A. Underline the limiting adjectives in each sentence. Do not include articles.

1. The pentathlon is a competition of five events.

2. All the events are held in one day.

3. The first event is the broad jump.

4. Throwing the javelin is the second test.

5. Before throwing the javelin, the athlete takes several steps.

6. Each athlete must also throw a discus.

7. A discus is a round metal or wooden object weighing four pounds.

8. Athletes hold it in one hand and spin before releasing it.

9. A decathlon has ten events.

10. It is held over a period of two days.

B. Complete each sentence with a limiting adjective. Do not include articles.

1. The Olympics are held every _____ years.

2. A gold medal is the _____ prize.

3. The _____ prize is silver.

4. Bronze is given to the _____ winner.

5. There are _____ rings on the Olympic flag.

6. _____ athletes don't win medals.

7. But _____ athletes are proud just to be there.

8. _____ members of teams receive individual medals.

9. _____ country should be proud of its athletes.

10. _____ athletes and coaches march in the parade.

Position of Adjectives

Exercise 37

The usual position of an adjective is before the noun it modifies.

An adjective complement follows a linking verb. It completes the meaning of a linking verb and describes the subject.

A. Underline the adjectives in the usual position.

1. The padded mitt helps the catcher.

2. A webbed glove is used by the first baseman.

3. The metal mask protects the face of the catcher.

4. His spiked shoes help him run on the muddy field.

5. Baseball gloves are made from genuine leather.

B. Underline the adjective complement in each sentence.

1. The catcher's mitt is padded.

2. The first baseman's glove is webbed.

3. The mask is metal.

4. The shoes are spiked.

5. Baseball gloves are leather.

C. Rewrite each sentence using the italicized adjective as an adjective complement.

1. The *confident* pitcher struck out ten batters.

_____

2. In the game, the *nervous* batter hit a home run.

_____

3. The *dry* field needed rain.

_____

D. Underline the adjectives in the usual position. Circle the adjective complements.

1. The old baseball was dirty and worn.

2. The blue and gray thread around the cork center is unraveled.

3. Under the thread, the black and red material is rubber.

4. The stitched cover is cowhide.

5. The larger softball is softer.

Comparison of Adjectives

Exercise 38

> Adjectives can be used to compare two or more persons or things.
>
> The positive degree expresses a quality about one person or thing or one group of persons or things.
>
> The comparative degree compares two persons or things.
>
> The superlative degree compares three or more persons or things.

A. Write on the line whether the italicized adjective is in the
P—positive, **C**—comparative, or **S**—superlative degree.

_____ 1. Karate is one of the *earliest* forms of unarmed combat.

_____ 2. It is the *most graceful* of the martial arts.

_____ 3. "Open hand" is the *closest* translation for the word "karate."

_____ 4. Chinese karate, kung fu, stresses *circular* hand movements.

_____ 5. Korean karate, tae kwon do, uses *more powerful* kicking movements.

_____ 6. The *safe* use of karate in America is for self-defense.

_____ 7. Karate experts are those with the *greatest* knowledge and control.

B. Complete each sentence with the adjective in the correct degree of comparison.

high—*superlative*   1. The _____ belt is the black belt.

low—*positive*   2. The beginner's, or _____ , belt is white.

great—*comparative* 3. The _____ the control, the better the match.

tough—*comparative* 4. _____ hands are the reward of practice.

little—*positive*   5. A _____ knowledge is a dangerous thing.

old—*comparative*   6. The _____ man won the match.

C. Write each phrase in the correct column.

| smoothest move | graceful jab | loudest yell | tiny child |
| higher kick | careless slap | quicker blow | whiter robe |

positive	**comparative**	**superlative**
_____	_____	_____
_____	_____	_____
_____	_____	

Review of Adjectives

Exercise 39

Complete the paragraph by choosing the appropriate adjectives.

| spicy | juicy | fresh | crisp | creamy |
| flaky | chilled | crunchy | stuffed | delicious |

(1–10.) Athletes from various countries sat together and ate a _____

meal. They began with a _____ salad and a _____

fruit cup with a _____ sauce. They shared _____ pizza

slices, _____juicy_____ hamburgers, tacos in _____ shells, and

_____ baked potatoes. Picking only one of the _____

French pastries was difficult. They seemed to drink gallons of _____

milk. Friendships were formed during this meal.

Write the proper adjective for the country that is famous for each type of food.

11. _____ spaghetti (Italy)

12. _____ waffles (Belgium)

13. _____ pastries (France)

14. _____ chop suey (China)

15. _____ potato salad (Germany)

16. _____ sausage (Poland)

17. _____ enchiladas (Mexico)

18. _____ fondue (Switzerland)

19. _____ sushi (Japan)

20. _____ goulash (Hungary)

Complete each sentence with the correct article.

21. _____ athlete eats a balanced diet.

22. _____ balanced diet is important to his training.

23. Eating correctly provides his body with _____ energy to compete.

Review of Adjectives

Exercise 39, continued

Complete each sentence with the correct demonstrative adjective.

24. The coach said, " _____ *(near)* balanced diets come from the five food groups."

25. Foods cannot be taken only from _____ *(far)* group.

Circle the correct word in parentheses.

26. (Your, You're) body gets vitamins A and C from fruits and vegetables.

27. (It's, Its) important to get vitamin B from breads and cereals.

28. Milk and cheese provide calcium for (your, you're) body.

29. (Your, You're) in need of iron from meat, fish, and poultry.

30. You can eat sweets and fats but (they're, their) needed only in small amounts.

Write on the line whether each italicized adjective is in the **P**—positive, **C**—comparative, or **S**—superlative degree.

_____ 31. Terri was the *smallest* athlete at the Olympics.

_____ 32. But on the balance beam, she was *braver* than all of them.

_____ 33. On the uneven bars, she showed *powerful* moves.

_____ 34. All of the athletes had the *highest* respect for her.

_____ 35. Her friendliness was one of her *stronger* gifts.

Complete each sentence with an adjective complement.

36. A weight lifter is _____ .

37. In the pool, the American swimmer was _____ .

38. The scores for the diver were _____ .

39. Was the pole vaulter _____ ?

40. The marathon runner was _____ when she finished.

Recognizing Action Verbs

Exercise 40

A verb is a word used to express action or being.

A. Circle the action verb in each sentence.

1. An emperor of India ⟨built⟩ the Taj Mahal.

2. The Taj Mahal contains the body of his wife.

3. People visit this tomb today.

4. Bees buzzed around the flowers in the garden.

5. Our class recited the poem during the assembly.

6. The motor sputtered to a stop.

7. A drought ruins farmland.

8. The reckless cars collided at the corner.

9. Scientists study the causes of diseases.

10. The deer dashed into the woods.

11. Many ships dock at the ports of Philadelphia.

12. The cows grazed contentedly in the fields.

13. The eager boy raced toward the finish line.

14. Alexandre-Gustave Eiffel designed the famous tower in Paris.

B. Complete each sentence with an action verb.

1. The boy _____ his dog on the head.

2. The cowboy _____ his horse for the rodeo.

3. The doctor_____ his patient.

4. The magician _____ many tricks.

5. The jet plane_____ in the airport.

6. Jeff _____ his lunch and went out to play.

7. Cars and trucks _____ air pollution.

8. Spiders _____ lacy webs.

9. My father _____ the kitchen a bright yellow.

10. The bubbles _____ as they rose in the air.

Writing Action Verbs

Exercise 41

A. Complete each sentence with an action verb.

1. Babies _____ when they're hungry.

2. The dog _____ the hole to bury the bone.

3. The mother _____ the child on the swing.

4. The mouse _____ across the kitchen floor.

5. You must _____ your homework each night.

6. Athletes _____ each day.

7. Let's go to the beach and _____ our kites.

8. On Saturday, Father usually _____ the lawn.

9. Please _____ me the salt and pepper.

10. When the bell rang at noon, we _____ our lunch.

11. We all _____ "Happy Birthday."

12. The watch _____ at three o'clock each afternoon.

13. His dog _____ at strangers.

14. Plants _____ sunlight in order to live.

15. _____ the window, because it's beginning to rain.

16. Jamie _____ his book every night.

B. Write sentences using each verb.

giggle   1. _____

tumble   2. _____

ride   3. _____

play   4. _____

jog   5. _____

grasp   6. _____

scream   7. _____

Writing Verbs

Exercise 42

A. Write an action word (verb) that each person, animal, or thing can perform.

1. puppies _____eat_____   11. flowers _____

2. birds _____   12. horses _____

3. children _____   13. cars _____

4. students _____   14. balloons _____

5. rock groups _____   15. clocks _____

6. authors _____   16. tires _____

7. babies _____   17. bunnies _____

8. athletes _____   18. birds _____

9. cows _____   19. dishes _____

10. boats _____   20. windows _____

B. Complete each sentence with a word from the list.

cried   yelled   said   whispered   answered
called   responded   exclaimed   gasped   replied

1. "You're out!" _____yelled_____ the umpire.

2. Mother _____, "Don't wake the baby."

3. Dad _____, "You dented my new car!"

4. "Anyone who passed the test has no homework," _____ the
   teacher.

5. "I cut my finger," _____ Debbie.

6. "My mother isn't home," _____ Rick.

7. "Look out behind you!" _____ Kyle.

8. The bank robber _____, "Give me all your money!"

9. "I give up," _____ the wrestler.

10. "It's time for dinner," _____ Mother.

Verbs of Being

Exercise 43

A verb is a word used to express action or being. The most common being verbs are *is, are, was, were, has been, have been, had been, will be, shall be.*

A. Circle the being verb in each sentence.

1. Disney World (is) in Florida.

2. Bubble gum is harmful to your teeth.

3. Good health habits are important.

4. State highways will be well traveled during the holidays.

5. Air pollution has been a problem in big cities.

6. These berries were poisonous.

7. Hoover Dam is one of the highest dams in the world.

8. Sunshine and water were necessary to grow these plants.

9. The twins were identical in every way.

10. Sports have been an important form of recreation in the United States.

11. Philadelphia is the city of Brotherly Love.

12. Diamonds are the hardest mineral known to man.

13. Green is a very restful color.

14. Citrus fruit is a good source of vitamin C.

B. Underline the being verbs in the paragraph.

   Venice is a famous Italian city. There are no streets in Venice. Instead, there are canals. Canals are waterways used for travel. The biggest canal is the Grand Canal. It is the "Main Street" of Venice. The center of activity in Venice is St. Mark's Square. This is a large area near St. Mark's Cathedral. People are always there, even late at night. In Venice, boats are the chief means of transportation. An old-fashioned boat is a gondola. Gondoliers are the people who operate the boats. Today, gondolas are boats for tourists. Boats with motors are the means of transportation for the citizens. Venice is an interesting and unusual city to visit.

Verbs and Sentences

Exercise 44

> The verb is a very important word in the sentence. Every sentence must have a verb.
> Sometimes a verb alone forms a sentence.

A. Write **S** before each group of words that is a sentence. Write **NS** before each group of words that is not a sentence.

___NS___ 1. The crab on the sandy beach.

_____ 2. I like to collect seashells.

_____ 3. Hot-air balloons in the sky.

_____ 4. Cheerleaders shouted for their team.

_____ 5. The team scored a touchdown.

_____ 6. Excitement in the air.

_____ 7. Some flowers bloom in the early spring.

_____ 8. Please stand.

_____ 9. A country scene by the artist.

_____ 10. Look behind you!

_____ 11. Last year, I caught three fish.

_____ 12. Leaves on our street.

_____ 13. A shrill echo in the night.

_____ 14. Jonathan feeds the birds leftover bread.

_____ 15. The artist painted a country scene with oil paints.

B. Add an action verb (and other words) to each group of words to form sentences.

1. Many new children _____

2. A strong wind _____

3. A colorful striped umbrella _____

4. Many interesting stories _____

5. The strange old mansion on the hill _____

Verb Phrases

Exercise 45

A verb phrase is a group of words that does the work of a single verb.

A. Underline the verb phrase in each sentence. Write on the lines the auxiliary verb(s) and the principal verb.

	aux. verb	prin. verb
1. Palm trees <u>will grow</u> in warm climates.	will	grow
2. Regular exercise is needed for good health.		
3. The student had forgotten about the test.		
4. Diamonds have been used in industry.		
5. The Plymouth colony was founded by the Pilgrims.		
6. The detective has solved the mystery.		
7. Ron's friends have gone to the shore.		
8. We should finish our work on time.		
9. Her brother is going home.		
10. Two highways will be connected by the new road.		
11. Each child may take two turns.		
12. A new television has been bought by our family.		
13. We have finished the color wheel in art class.		
14. You have earned a reward.		
15. Early weapons were made of stone.		

B. Write sentences using each verb phrase.

was given   1. _____

might go   2. _____

have studied   3. _____

will finish   4. _____

were playing   5. _____

may contain   6. _____

are known   7. _____

Verb Phrases in Questions and Negative Statements

Exercise 46

> In questions and negative statements the parts of the verb phrase may be separated.

A. Underline the principal verb and the auxiliary verb in each sentence.

1. The new student in our class <u>does</u> not <u>speak</u> English.

2. Have you ordered the pizza yet?

3. Are you interested in sharing my cupcakes?

4. I will not forget your birthday.

5. The pyramids were not built in a day.

6. I am not interested in going to the game.

7. Do you remember my address?

8. Solar energy is not used by many people.

9. Have you thanked them for the gift?

10. Do you understand the directions on the test?

11. Did you oversleep this morning?

12. Has anyone written the party invitations?

13. Marsha will not be responsible for the damages.

14. Does anyone know this puppy's name?

15. Why did you follow that plan?

B. Answer each question with a negative response. Underline the principal verb and the auxiliary verb in the question and response.

1. Did you watch the late movie last night?

_____

2. Could you eat an entire pizza by yourself?

_____

3. Are you playing cards with your brother?

_____

4. Will you dance for eight hours without stopping?

_____

Regular and Irregular Verbs

Exercise 47

A verb has three principal parts: the present, the past, and the past participle.

A regular verb forms its past and its past participle by adding -d or -ed to the present.

An irregular verb does not form its past and past participle by adding -d or -ed to the present.

A. Write the past and past participle of each verb.

	past	**past participle**
1. cheer		
2. am		
3. play		
4. make		
5. fall		
6. roll		
7. do		
8. rise		
9. giggle		
10. write		

B. Write whether each verb is regular or irregular.

1. talk		11. explore	
2. push		12. see	
3. come		13. do	
4. hurt		14. compare	
5. serve		15. take	
6. teach		16. smile	
7. look		17. sink	
8. know		18. lay	
9. grow		19. stand	
10. carry		20. skip	

Recognizing Regular and Irregular Verbs

Exercise 48

A. Underline the verb or verb phrase in each sentence. Write whether the principal verb is regular or irregular.

_____ 1. Recently, our class took a trip to the Vietnam War Memorial.

_____ 2. The memorial is located in Washington, D.C.

_____ 3. It was built in honor of the Vietnam War veterans.

_____ 4. The names of all the veterans are written in stone.

_____ 5. Family members and friends often visit the memorial.

_____ 6. They find the name of their deceased loved one.

_____ 7. Often, they leave flowers at the site.

_____ 8. The flowers are a sign of remembrance.

_____ 9. The memorial makes a lasting impression on each visitor.

_____ 10. We have learned to appreciate the soldiers' sacrifices.

B. Write sentences using each verb. Write on the line whether the verb is **R**—regular or **I**—irregular.

_____ 1. took _____

_____ 2. ate _____

_____ 3. laughed _____

_____ 4. walked _____

_____ 5. studied _____

_____ 6. made _____

_____ 7. answered _____

_____ 8. knew _____

_____ 9. painted _____

_____ 10. talk _____

Writing Regular and Irregular Verbs

Exercise 49

A. Complete each sentence with the past or past participle of the verb. Remember to use the past participle if the sentence has an auxiliary verb.

measure   1. Scientists have _____ rainwater for years.

call   2. They use an instrument_____ a rain guage.

collect   3. The rain is _____ in a bucket.

stop   4. When the rain has _____ , they can measure it.

use   5. A ruler is _____ to tell how deep the water is.

spin   6. A spider has _____ a lacy web on our fence.

collect   7. During the night, dewdrops _____ on the web.

sparkle   8. The dewdrops_____ in the early morning sunlight.

B. Complete each sentence with the past or the past participle of the verb. Fill in the puzzle with the answers.

fall   1. Mike had _____ from his bike twice.

grow   2. The plant_____ two inches since last week.

give   3. I had _____ my catcher's mitt to my friend.

go   4. Who _____ to the game yesterday?

teach   5. Our teacher had _____ us how to do long division.

try   6. We _____ that solution to the equation.

jump   7. The athlete _____ rope for exercise.

stand   8. The fans _____ in line for the concert tickets.

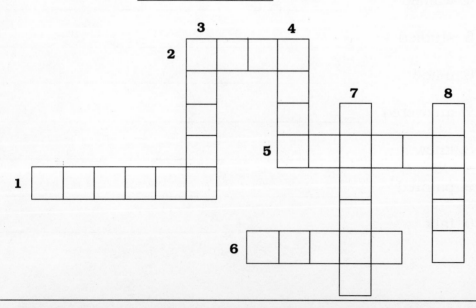

Forms of *Break*; Forms of *See*

Exercise 50

> The principal parts of the verb *break* are *break, broke, has broken*. *Break* is the present form. *Broke* is the past form. *Has broken* is the past participle. The past participle is used with auxiliary verbs such as *have, has,* and *had.*
>
> The principal parts of the verb *see* are *see, saw, has seen*. *See* is the present form. *Saw* is the past form. *Has seen* is the past participle. The past participle is used with auxiliary verbs such as *have, has,* and *had.*

A. Complete each sentence with the correct form of the verb *break.*

1. Have you _____ your pencil point?

2. _____ the eggs into the bowl.

3. Jean has _____ the good plate.

4. Rick had _____ the rule.

5. The scouts _____ camp and departed.

6. Who _____ the window?

7. If you _____ the law, you will be punished.

8. He never _____ a promise.

9. Beth has _____ her front tooth.

10. I will not _____ a promise.

B. Complete each sentence with the correct form of the verb *see.*

1. Yesterday, I _____ the state capitol.

2. In the story *A Christmas Carol,* Scrooge _____ Marley's ghost.

3. Our family has _____ the Rocky Mountains.

4. Have you _____ my gloves?

5. Nobody _____ the accident take place.

6. Have you _____ the play before?

7. Our class _____ the new exhibit at the art museum.

8. Did you ever _____ the Washington Monument?

9. I have never _____ the dinosaur display.

10. Do you _____ what I _____ ?

Forms of *Go*; Forms of *Choose*

Exercise 51

> The principal parts of the verb *go* are *go, went, has gone.* *Go* is the present form. *Went* is the past form. *Has gone* is the past participle. The past participle is used with auxiliary verbs such as *have, has,* and *had.*
>
> The principal parts of the verb *choose* are *choose, chose, has chosen.* *Choose* is the present form. *Chose* is the past form. *Has chosen* is the past participle. The past participle is used with auxiliary verbs such as *have, has,* and *had.*

A. Complete each sentence with the correct form of the verb *go.*

1. Have the students _____ on their class trip yet?

2. _____ immediately, boys.

3. Last night my father _____ to a baseball game.

4. All my brothers _____ to college.

5. Has Mark _____ for the newspaper?

6. Columbus _____ to the Spanish court for money.

7. Winter is here; the birds have _____ .

8. My mother has _____ to the hairdresser.

9. Jean _____ the wrong way.

10. They _____ to the swimming pool every day.

B. Complete each sentence with the correct form of the verb *choose.*

1. Each boy has _____ his favorite story.

2. _____ any book you wish to read.

3. I _____ the blue flag to carry in the parade.

4. The singer has _____ my favorite song to sing.

5. Has the club _____ its president?

6. _____ your friends carefully.

7. The coach _____ two girls as leaders.

8. We have _____ a new name for our school newspaper.

9. Whom did you _____ ?

10. I had _____ Lynn.

Forms of *Take*

Exercise 52

> The principal parts of the verb *take* are *take, took, has taken*. *Take* is the present form. *Took* is the past form. *Has taken* is the past participle. The past participle is used with auxiliary verbs such as *have, has,* and *had.*

A. Complete each sentence with the correct form of the verb *take.*

1. Rudy has _____ our equipment to the gym.

2. That quotation is _____ from the Declaration of Independence.

3. _____ care of your health.

4. Mario always_____ his little brother with him.

5. We _____ a jet plane to Washington last year.

6. Have you _____ your medicine?

7. _____ the bottle from the baby.

8. Many citizens _____ part in the drive against cerebral palsy.

9. _____ out two sheets of paper for the test.

10. Ted has_____ the test for the Naval Academy.

B. Circle the correct form of the verb *take* in parentheses.

1. The witness has (took, taken) the oath in court.

2. It (took, take) four years to build that skyscraper.

3. Jack quickly (taken, took) the sharp scissors from the child.

4. Please (taken, take) your umbrella to school, Carrie.

5. I have never (took, taken) that route to the city.

C. Write sentences using each form of the verb *take.*

present   1. _____

_____

past   2. _____

_____

past participle 3. _____

_____

Name

Review of Verb Forms

PROPERTY OF
HANOVER TOWNSHIP BOARD OF EDUCATION
CEDAR KNOLLS, NEW JERSEY

Exercise 53

> Both the past and the past participle may be used to tell past time. If there is no auxiliary verb, use the past. If there is an auxiliary verb, use the past participle.

A. Complete each sentence with the past or past participle of the verb.

choose   1. The class _____ Michael as president.

sign   2. The union has _____ the contract.

flash   3. A bright light _____ in the darkness.

join   4. My brother has _____ the army reserve.

fold   5. We _____ the sheets as they came from the dryer.

do   6. They have _____ their work well.

lie   7. Leaves _____ on the ground like a colorful blanket.

sit   8. The campers _____ around the fire and talked.

take   9. Have you _____ your walk today?

shake   10. An earthquake _____ the city of Santa Barbara.

fall   11. Leaves have _____ into the gutter.

teach   12. The faculty _____ the children well.

enter   13. Meg carefully _____ the program into the computer.

throw   14. Roger _____ the bone to his dog.

break   15. Mark has _____ the chain on his bike.

B. Write sentences using each verb.

has hurt   1. _____

_____

bought   2. _____

_____

have seen   3. _____

_____

sank   4. _____

_____

Simple Tenses

Exercise 54

> The tense of a verb shows the time of its action.
>
> The present tense tells about an action that is happening now or that happens again and again.
>
> The past tense tells about an action that has happened.
>
> The future tense tells about an action that will happen.

A. Underline the verb or verb phrase in each sentence. Write the tense on the line.

_____ 1. The president resides in the White House.

_____ 2. The jogger puffed alarmingly.

_____ 3. Another touchdown will put our team in the lead.

_____ 4. Here comes the parade around the corner.

_____ 5. Soon the helicopter will land on the roof.

_____ 6. The airplane carried relief supplies to the flood victims.

_____ 7. The audience watched the figure skaters intently.

_____ 8. The train will not leave until the afternoon.

_____ 9. The music teacher will teach the class a new song.

_____ 10. The birds flew south for the winter.

B. Complete each sentence with the correct form of the verb.

use—*present* 1. The weather service _____ first names to identify hurricanes.

see—*future* 2. Look up and you _____ cloud formations.

go—*future* 3. The sun _____ out someday—billions of years in the future.

walk—*past* 4. Astronauts _____ on the moon on July 20, 1969.

deposit—*present* 5. A river _____ mud at its mouth.

study—*present* 6. Scientists _____ the movement of planets.

is—*present* 7. Asbestos _____ an inflammable mineral.

look—*present* 8. Asbestos _____ like white hair on a rock.

Linking Verbs

Exercise 55

A linking verb links a noun, a pronoun, or an adjective with the subject.

A. Circle the subjective complement in each sentence. Write on the line whether it is a noun, a pronoun, or an adjective. The linking verbs are italicized.

_____ 1. The orange *is* a fruit that contains vitamin C.

_____ 2. Those mountains *are* very rocky.

_____ 3. The winner *was* he.

_____ 4. Wayne *is* the winner of the race.

_____ 5. Boston *is* a large city in Massachusetts.

_____ 6. My cousin Susie *is* the youngest in her family.

_____ 7. Joan and Marla *will be* partners in the parade.

_____ 8. The noisiest girl at recess *was* she.

_____ 9. The milk I poured on my cereal *was* sour.

_____ 10. Amelia Earhart *is* a well-known female pilot.

_____ 11. Wind *is* air in motion.

_____ 12. I *am* a tall person.

B. Complete each sentence with a subjective complement. Use nouns, pronouns, or adjectives.

1. My dog is _____ when she is fed.

2. Salt and pepper are _____ we use every day.

3. Swimming has been my favorite _____ .

4. Chicken pox is a _____ that affects children.

5. A gold chain will be my _____ to Sue for her birthday.

6. Pancakes and sausage is my favorite _____ .

7. New York City is a _____ you should visit.

8. Jupiter is the largest _____ in the universe.

Transitive Verbs

Exercise 56

A transitive verb expresses an action that passes from a doer to a receiver.

A. Underline the transitive verb in each sentence. Write the receiver on the line.

_____ 1. The girl made costumes for the Halloween party.

_____ 2. Our class wrote letters to our state senators.

_____ 3. The high winds broke the window in our living room.

_____ 4. Henry Hudson discovered the Hudson River.

_____ 5. I burned the toast this morning.

_____ 6. A fifth-grade boy drew this picture.

_____ 7. The hunter shot the black bear.

_____ 8. The cat chased the mouse across the kitchen.

_____ 9. Dorothy answered the question correctly.

_____ 10. The Marine raised the flag during the ceremony.

_____ 11. The car hit the pole on the corner.

_____ 12. Matt walks the dog each evening after dinner.

B. Complete each sentence with a receiver of the action.

1. Babies eat _____.

2. The two boys ride _____.

3. Squirrels eat _____.

4. Farmers plant _____.

5. My kittens drink _____.

6. The farmer's chickens lay _____.

7. Eskimos build _____.

8. Most artists paint _____.

Intransitive Verbs

Exercise 57

> An intransitive verb has no receiver of the action.

A. Circle the intransitive verb in each sentence. Underline the doer of the action.

1. The sunbeams danced in the window pane.

2. Two boats raced down the river during the pageant.

3. Earnest students work hard every day.

4. The hikers waded through the swamp and up the hill.

5. The news spread quickly through the town.

6. We often swim in that lake in the mountains.

7. Those birds return each year to our tree.

8. The young men talk together on the corner.

9. The train sped by the station.

10. Each hour the bus stops at our corner.

11. The frisky puppy played in the snow.

12. Pretty flowers grow in that garden by the lake.

13. A log floated downstream toward the clearing.

14. I live in an apartment in the city.

B. Complete each sentence with an adverb or prepositional phrase. Circle the intransitive verb.

1. The army advanced _____

2. The boys sat _____

3. My hat blew _____

4. The people watched _____

5. Michael called _____

6. The coach yelled _____

7. The athletes jogged _____

8. The birds flew _____

9. The runners puffed _____

Transitive and Intransitive Verbs

Exercise 58

A. Write on the line whether the italicized verb is transitive or intransitive.

_____ 1. Last summer, our family *went* to Disney World.

_____ 2. The plane *left* the airport on time.

_____ 3. In the air, we *soared* above the clouds.

_____ 4. The pilot *landed* the plane smoothly in Florida.

_____ 5. At the hotel, we *unpacked* our bags.

_____ 6. Hurriedly, we *headed* for the park.

_____ 7. We *had* so much fun.

_____ 8. All of us *slept* peacefully at the end of the day.

_____ 9. We all *had* dreams of the days to come.

_____ 10. Maybe my family *can go* to Disneyland next year.

B. Underline the verb in each sentence. Write on the line whether the verb is **T**—transitive or **I**—intransitive.

_____ 1. Jay writes well.

_____ 2. The children sat on the curb.

_____ 3. Most people like the circus.

_____ 4. I walk to school every day.

_____ 5. The students read their essays to the class.

_____ 6. I rake leaves every Saturday morning in the fall.

_____ 7. Danny recommended this book.

_____ 8. The usher took my ticket.

_____ 9. Many people jog each day.

_____ 10. I talk to my friend on the phone every night.

Agreement of Subject with Verb

Exercise 59

> A subject and a verb must always agree.
>
> A singular noun and the singular subject pronouns *he, she,* and *it* must always have a singular verb. A singular verb ends in *s* or *es* in the present tense. Plural nouns and the plural subject pronouns *we* and *they* must always have a plural verb. A plural verb does not end in *s* or *es*. The pronouns *I* and *you* also take a verb without an *s* or *es* ending in the present tense.

A. Circle the correct verb form in parentheses. The subject is italicized.

1. Once a week our school *cafeteria* (serve, serves) pizza for lunch.

2. A huge oak *tree* (stand, stands) in the corner of our yard.

3. In the early spring, *birds* (build, builds) their nests.

4. The team's *captain* (meet, meets) regularly with the players.

5. The *San Andreas Fault* in California periodically (shift, shifts).

6. The school dress *code* (is, are) given in this book.

7. The *baby* (seem, seems) to be hungry.

8. This *book* of mystery stories (is, are) interesting.

9. Each year my *family* (visit, visits) my grandmother in Ireland.

10. *Flocks* of birds (fly, flies) south each fall.

11. Rainy *days* (is, are) good days to read.

12. Each Saturday the baseball *team* (play, plays) a game.

13. This *plant* (bloom, blooms) every spring.

14. *Weathermen* (predict, predicts) the weather through scientific methods.

15. My *dog* (like, likes) to play in the snow.

B. Circle the correct verb in parentheses. Add words to make a complete sentence.

1. fish (swim, swims) _____

2. sun (shine, shines) _____

3. ghosts (haunt, haunts) _____

4. waves (splash, splashes) _____

5. wind (blow, blows) _____

6. candy (taste, tastes) _____

Is, Are, and Am

Exercise 60

> The forms of the verb *be* in the present tense are *is*, *are*, and *am*.
>
> Use *is* when the subject is a singular noun or with the singular subject pronouns *he, she, it*.
>
> Use *are* when the subject is plural or with the subject pronouns *we, you, they*.
>
> Use *am* with the subject pronoun *I*.

A. Circle the correct form of the verb *be* in parentheses.

1. Nancy (is, are) the youngest girl in the class.

2. (Is, Are) you hungry?

3. I (is, am) the oldest child in my family.

4. When (is, are) you coming home from camp?

5. (Is, Are) you old enough to be on the hockey team?

6. The first-grade students (is, are) in the schoolyard playing.

7. (Is, Are) Alaska the largest state?

8. Cows (is, are) grazing in the field.

9. In the summer, the days (is, are) long.

10. I (is, am) doing a project on seals for science.

11. Moderate exercise (is, are) good for your health.

B. Complete each sentence with *is*, *are*, or *am*.

1. Your friends _____ here.

2. The llama _____ a beast of burden.

3. The nails in this board _____ rusty.

4. I _____ the wolf in *Peter and the Wolf.*

5. This _____ my friend Juan.

6. _____ the flowers in that basket from your garden?

7. That book _____ mine.

8. _____ you tired after your football game?

9. Those boys _____ active.

10. Where _____ you going, Robert?

Was and Were

Exercise 61

> The forms of the verb *be* in the past tense are *was* and *were*.
>
> Use *was* when the subject is a singular noun or with the singular subject pronouns *I, he, she, it.*
>
> Use *were* when the subject is plural or with the subject pronouns *we, you, they.*

A. Circle the correct verb in parentheses.

1. (Was, Were) Jeff with you?

2. (Was, Were) you on the team last year?

3. He (was, were) not at home yesterday.

4. The rides at the amusement park (was, were) free.

5. Sandy (was, were) very courteous to the store owner.

6. The final exam (was, were) difficult.

7. The boys (was, were) at the football game.

8. (Was, Were) all your classmates with you?

9. Girls from the class (was, were) in the gym.

10. Lewis and Clark (was, were) explorers.

11. Flatboats (was, were) an early means of transportation.

12. Many of the Kennedy brothers (was, were) involved in politics.

B. Complete each sentence with *was* or *were*.

1. The children _____ surprised.

2. _____ you on the roller coaster?

3. The old table _____ too shaky to use.

4. The books _____ on the shelf in the library.

5. Her hands _____ cold from throwing snowballs.

6. The room in the attic _____ dark.

7. You_____ here first, Ken.

8. The gates to the mansion _____ open.

9. My grandfather_____ once a fisherman.

10. _____ you at the concert, Lynn?

Doesn't and Don't

Exercise 62

> Use *doesn't* when the subject is a singular noun or with the singular subject pronouns *he, she, it.*
>
> Use *don't* when the subject is plural or with the subject pronuns *I, we, you, they.*

A. Circle the correct verb in parentheses. Write it on the line.

_____ 1. This chair (doesn't, don't) match the other chairs.

_____ 2. (Doesn't, don't) this book belong to you?

_____ 3. Alex (doesn't, don't) live near us.

_____ 4. We (doesn't, don't) need more candy.

_____ 5. Why (doesn't, don't) Judy hurry?

_____ 6. My sister (doesn't, don't) sing in the choir.

_____ 7. It (doesn't, don't) suit Colleen.

_____ 8. The key (doesn't, don't) fit in the lock.

_____ 9. (Doesn't, Don't) you remember the answer?

_____ 10. Why (doesn't, don't) Anne make her bed?

B. Complete each sentence with *doesn't* or *don't.*

1. Those curtains _____ hang gracefully.

2. That subway train _____ stop here.

3. _____ that music have a good beat?

4. The shelves in this cabinet _____ fit.

5. _____ you remember my name?

6. _____ Dawn play the drums?

7. _____ you want this pen?

8. These flowers _____ bloom until summer.

9. He _____ write very well.

10. _____ he look sad?

Name

Let and *Leave*

The verb *let (let, has let)* means to permit or to allow. The verb *leave (left, has left)* means to depart or to go away from.

A. Circle the correct verb in parentheses.

1. Jason will soon (let, leave) for camp.

2. Sandra has (left, let) the beach to go home.

3. How soon will you (let, leave)?

4. (Leave, Let) kind thoughts be always in your mind.

5. My uncle (let, left) for San Francisco yesterday.

6. Will Mother (let, leave) us go to the party?

7. The mail carrier (let, left) the mail under the door.

8. The farmer (left, let) the pumpkins in the field.

9. (Leave, Let) them go now.

10. (Leave, Let) the package here with me.

B. Complete each sentence with the correct form of *let* or *leave*.

1. _____ me read your copy of *Sounder.*

2. _____ your packages on the porch.

3. Kurt, please _____ the paper on my desk.

4. _____ us help Mother with the dishes.

5. Brian has not _____ for school yet.

6. The astronaut _____ the spaceship to explore the planet.

7. My father _____ me go to the speech tournament on Saturday.

8. The president will _____ for Germany next week.

9. My parents won't _____ me have a dirt bike.

10. The teacher _____ the students talk quietly in the classroom.

C. Write sentences using each verb.

leave   1. _____

left   2. _____

let   3. _____

Name _____

Lie and *Lay*

Exercise 64

> The verb *lie (lay, has lain)* means to rest. The verb *lay (laid, has laid)* means to put or to place in position.

A. Circle the correct verb in parentheses.

1. Grandmother often (lays, lies) down to rest in the afternoon.

2. Today I (lay, laid) the mail on the table beside the phone.

3. The maid (laid, lay) the towels on the rack in the bathroom.

4. Pigs sometimes (lie, lay) in the soft, warm mud.

5. I (laid, lay) the spoon on the table.

6. People often (lay, lie) flowers on the graves of their loved ones.

7. The children usually (lay, lie) down for an afternoon nap.

8. (Lie, Lay) that box in the corner, please.

9. She had (lain, laid) awake all night.

10. The pumpkins have (lain, laid) on the snow-covered field for a week.

B. Complete each sentence with the correct form of *lie* or *lay*.

1. We _____ on the beach every weekend.

2. Soil _____ all over the floor where the plant fell.

3. _____ on the grass with me and watch the clouds go by.

4. If we _____ in the sun too long, we'll burn.

5. We had _____ in bed too long this morning.

6. My dog _____ on the back porch and waited for me.

7. Will you _____ this paper on the teacher's desk?

8. The accident victim has _____ in a coma for days.

9. Multicolored shells _____ on the beach.

10. _____ the dessert fork next to the dinner fork.

C. Write sentences using each verb.

lie   1. _____

lay (put)   2. _____

has laid   3. _____

Sit and Set

Exercise 65

> The verb *sit (sat, has sat)* means to have a place or to keep a seat.
> The verb *set (set, has set)* means to place or to fix in position.

A. Circle the correct verb in parentheses.

1. We (sit, set) the trophy on the top shelf.

2. I (set, sit) across from my little sister at the dinner table.

3. The dog (sat, set) on the steps waiting for me.

4. I (set, sit) the glass on the table without a coaster.

5. Eskimos (sit, set) traps for animals.

6. The children usually (sit, set) in the back seat of the car.

7. The president has often (set, sat) at his desk in the oval office.

8. Robin, please (sit, set) the gift under the Christmas tree.

9. My sister always (sets, sits) too close to the television.

10. Where shall we (set, sit)?

B. Complete each sentence with the correct form of *sit* or *set.*

1. Who _____ there yesterday?

2. On warm evenings, we _____ on the porch.

3. _____ here and rest for a minute.

4. Where shall we _____ the bookcase?

5. Infants usually _____ in high chairs.

6. In school, I _____ near the teacher's desk.

7. _____ the table for dinner, please.

8. Grandfather always _____ in his favorite chair.

9. The nurse _____ up all night with the sick child.

10. _____ the books on the bottom shelf.

C. Write sentences using each verb.

sit   1. _____

sat   2. _____

set   3. _____

Teach and Learn

Exercise 66

> The verb *teach (taught, has taught)* means to give instruction or to pass knowledge on. The verb *learn (learned, has learned)* means to receive instruction or knowledge.

A. Circle the correct verb in parentheses.

1. My cousin (taught, learned) me how to skate.

2. Jim and Bruce (taught, learned) first aid in the Boy Scouts' program.

3. The mother bird (teaches, learns) the baby birds to fly.

4. The carpenter (learned, taught) Jennie to make a chair.

5. Yes, the coach (teaches, learns) us the rules.

6. I (learned, taught) how to bake a cake from Jessica.

7. (Learn, Teach) me to dance, Carmen.

8. The lifeguard (taught, learned) Sharon to dive.

9. Our new teacher (learned, taught) us how to write poetry.

10. Sara (taught, learned) to water-ski this summer.

B. Complete each sentence with the correct form of *teach* or *learn.*

1. Who _____ your dog that trick?

2. He _____ that trick from me.

3. I have _____ him several new tricks.

4. We _____ long division in fourth grade.

5. The class _____ about petroleum.

6. All students _____ the multiplication tables.

7. In school we _____ how to pronounce difficult words.

8. Have you_____ how to make that model airplane?

C. Write sentences using each verb.

teach 1. _____

learned 2. _____

taught 3. _____

Name

Troublesome Verbs

Exercise 67

A. Circle the correct verb in parentheses.

1. (Sit, Set) the dishes on the table for dinner, please.

2. Ron has (lain, laid) in the sun all morning.

3. My parents won't (let, leave) me attend the hockey game.

4. Many people (sit, set) on the beach to get a suntan.

5. If we don't (let, leave) now, we'll be late.

6. We (set, sat) up the tent in the new campsite.

7. Alvin has (teach, taught) me how to ride a skateboard.

8. I (learned, taught) to identify the plants of this area.

9. Cindy, (lie, lay) the packages on the table.

10. I can't (lay, lie) on this hard bench.

11. We (left, let) the concert during the intermission.

12. Our family has finally (set, sat) out for Cape Cod.

13. My parents (let, left) me have my own dog.

14. The bear (lay, laid) near her newborn cubs.

15. (Sit, Set) the atlas on the second shelf, please.

B. Write sentences using each verb.

has laid 1. _____

_____

set 2. _____

_____

taught 3. _____

_____

leave 4. _____

_____

lie 5. _____

_____

Review of Verbs

Complete the chart with the missing principal parts of the verb. In the last column, write whether the verb is regular or irregular.

	past	**past participle**	**regular/irregular**
1. break	_____	_____	_____
2. call	_____	_____	_____
3. like	_____	_____	_____
4. choose	_____	_____	_____
5. go	_____	_____	_____

Underline the verb phrase in each sentence.

6. Rick had run the fifty-meter race.

7. Did you pass your math test?

8. Will you take my project to the librarian?

9. Scientists can predict an earthquake in advance.

10. Our team did not win the soccer game.

Write on the line the tense of the italicized verb.

_____ 11. We *walked* along the beach at sunrise.

_____ 12. Susan *feeds* the dog twice a day.

_____ 13. These tulips *will bloom* in early spring.

_____ 14. Last week our class *visited* the airport.

_____ 15. The jumbo jet *taxied* down the runway.

Circle the correct verb in parentheses.

16. Edward (broke, broken) his new skateboard.

17. We had (saw, seen) this movie last year.

18. (Lie, Lay) down and take a rest, Brian.

19. Please (sit, set) the picture carefully on the piano.

20. Maggie (lay, laid) her keys on the coffee table.

Review of Verbs

Complete each sentence with the correct verb form.

21. My teacher _____ give us homework.   (doesn't, don't)

22. We _____ staying after school for practice.   (am, are)

23. Our dogs _____ to ride in the car.   (like, likes)

24. The team _____ ball in the back lot.   (play, plays)

25. The children _____ at the school assembly.   (was, were)

Write the subjective complement in each sentence in column A. In column B, write whether it is a noun, pronoun, or adjective. The linking verb is italicized.

	A	B
26. Next year, I *will be* captain of the squad.	_____	_____
27. The colors in that sunset *are* magnificent.	_____	_____
28. I *am* nervous in the dark.	_____	_____
29. It *was* she whom I saw.	_____	_____
30. Those sweaters *are* expensive.	_____	_____

Write on the line whether the italicized verb is transitive or intransitive.

_____ 31. The fire alarm *sounded* late last night.

_____ 32. Steve *walks* the dog after school.

_____ 33. The boat *sailed* into the sunset.

_____ 34. The storm *blew* the wires down.

_____ 35. I *left* my sunglasses on the beach.

_____ 36. This rose bush *bloomed* early in the summer.

_____ 37. The singer *signed* many autographs.

_____ 38. The audience *clapped* after the speech.

_____ 39. *Come* with me to the store, please.

_____ 40. The workers *built* the house in two weeks.

Adverbs of Time

Exercise 69

> An adverb modifies a verb, an adjective, or another adverb.
>
> Adverbs of time answer the question *when* or *how often.*
>
> Some adverbs of time are *again, already, always, before, early, finally, frequently, now, often, soon, today,* and *yesterday.*

A. Underline the adverb in each sentence that tells *when* or *how often.*

1. We often go sailing on Penn Lake.

2. My father rises early to avoid the morning traffic.

3. Please go to the store now.

4. The boat will return to the dock soon.

5. Sing that song again, Becky.

6. Ron always studies his lessons.

7. My brother and his family now live in Boston.

8. The mayor will sign the bill soon.

9. Always be kind, generous, and thoughtful.

10. Our class already visited Valley Forge.

11. The mail is delivered to each house daily.

12. Once you try this, you'll like it.

B. Complete each sentence with an adverb of time.

1. The train will leave _____.

2. I _____ think of the fun we had.

3. You must come _____ in order to get a seat.

4. The actor arrived _____ for the performance.

5. The old man _____ repeats his story.

6. Ruth _____ eats a lot when she is nervous.

7. You may leave _____.

8. I _____ enjoy a picnic in the park.

9. I never saw that _____.

10. _____ we went skating on the pond.

Adverbs of Place

Exercise 70

> Adverbs of place answer the question *where.*
>
> Some adverbs of place are *above, away, backward, below, down, forth, here, in, out, there,* and *up.*

A. Underline the adverb in each sentence that tells *where.*

1. Tina sat <u>there</u> on that bench.

2. A wonderful thing happened here.

3. The land slopes upward toward the cabin.

4. The soldiers marched forward into battle.

5. You may come in if your shoes are clean.

6. Step down, Robert, but be careful.

7. My parents have gone away for the weekend.

8. The parade moved on as scheduled.

9. Meet me inside , Sally.

10. The captain rode ahead of his troops.

11. Do not fall off the rolling log, Rick.

12. Trevor carried the baby upstairs to bed.

B. Complete each sentence with an adverb of place.

1. You will find Patty_____ near the stairs.

2. The deer darted _____ in front of the traffic.

3. The wind scattered the leaves _____ .

4. Place the table _____ .

5. The boat turned _____ toward the port.

6. The enemy crept _____ toward the fort.

7. Sit_____ , Michael.

8. You may walk _____ , if you wish.

9. The young man fell _____ .

10. Sammy took the dog _____ .

Adverbs of Manner

Exercise 71

Adverbs of manner answer the question *how*.

Some adverbs of manner are *carefully, correctly, fast, gracefully, hard, kindly, quickly, softly, swiftly, truthfully,* and *well*.

A. Underline the adverb in each sentence that tells *how* or *in what manner*.

1. Gina answered the teacher <u>politely</u>.

2. My sister sings beautifully.

3. The scholar worked diligently on the project.

4. The garden snake moves silently through the grass.

5. The bright campfire glowed steadily in the night.

6. Speak distinctly, Tommy.

7. The soldiers fought heroically at the Battle of Bull Run.

8. Jennifer carefully checked her answers on the test.

9. Heather drives cautiously in heavy traffic.

10. The pioneers suffered greatly from the harsh weather.

11. An efficient secretary will type well.

12. You have answered that question wisely.

B. Complete each sentence with an adverb of manner.

1. Listen _____ to what I say.

2. Jason draws and paints _____ .

3. We approached the cabin _____ .

4. Cannons roared _____ throughout the battle.

5. The wind howled _____ during the night.

6. The hungry alley cat ate _____ .

7. Our canoe floated _____ down the river.

8. The excited boys shouted _____ when their team won.

9. The bell rang _____ throughout the town.

10. The Italian chef cooks pasta _____ .

Review of Adverbs of Time, Place, and Manner

Exercise 72

A. Underline the adverb in each sentence. Write on the line whether it expresses time, place, or manner.

_____ 1. New York was once the capital of our country.

_____ 2. The frightened boy jumped back from the fire.

_____ 3. The crowd gathered quickly around the accident.

_____ 4. The school band marched proudly down the street.

_____ 5. Her blue eyes twinkled merrily.

_____ 6. The passenger ship finally reached port.

_____ 7. Richard answered the advertisement immediately.

_____ 8. The bus to Phoenix stops here.

_____ 9. The speedboat swiftly skimmed the water.

_____ 10. The frightened rabbit darted away.

_____ 11. We have hunted everywhere for my digital watch.

_____ 12. The farmer reached the market early.

_____ 13. I have met your uncle before.

_____ 14. The woman lifted the basket of eggs carefully.

_____ 15. Please sign your name here.

B. Write sentences using each adverb.

quickly   1. _____

inside   2. _____

finally   3. _____

yesterday   4. _____

truthfully   5. _____

forward   6. _____

Comparison of Adverbs

Exercise 73

Many adverbs have three degrees of comparison: positive, comparative, and superlative.

Some adverbs form the comparative degree by adding *-er*. They form the superlative by adding *-est*. Most of these adverbs have one or two syllables.

Most adverbs that end in *-ly* form the comparative by adding *more* before the positive. They form the superlative by adding *most* before the positive.

A. Underline the adverb in each sentence. Write on the line the degree of comparison.

    positive   1. Jennifer arrived home early.

_____ 2. The boys finished the job faster than the girls.

_____ 3. The puppy opened its eyes widest of all.

_____ 4. The teacher will read to us later in the day.

_____ 5. Roger spoke kindly to the blind man.

_____ 6. Frank worked hardest at math.

_____ 7. I live farther from school than you do.

_____ 8. Steve studied for this test earnestly.

_____ 9. A snail travels more slowly than many animals.

_____ 10. Of all the students, my sister dances most gracefully.

B. Circle the correct adverb in parentheses.

1. It is raining (harder, hardest) today than yesterday.

2. The sun shines (brightly, more brightly) than the other stars.

3. Eggs must be handled (carefully, more carefully) than other food.

4. The eagle soared (swiftly, more swiftly) overhead.

5. Handle the baby hamster (gently, most gently).

6. If we ride our bikes, we'll get to the park (faster, fastest).

7. We greeted the visitor (politely, more politely) and returned to our work.

8. The train should be arriving (soon, sooner).

Good and Well

Exercise 74

> The word *good* is an adjective. Adjectives modify nouns or pronouns. *Good* may also follow a linking verb as an adjective complement. *Good* answers the question *what kind.*
>
> The word *well* is an adverb. Adverbs usually modify verbs. *Well* modifies a verb and answers the question *how.*

A. Circle the correct word in parentheses.

1. Andy cleaned his room (good, well).

2. Follow that (good, well) advice.

3. (Good, Well) foods build healthy bodies.

4. Those are (good, well) pencil drawings.

5. Jeffrey prepares his lessons (good, well).

6. Canada and the United States are (good, well) neighbors.

7. Bananas grow (good, well) in that warm climate.

8. Our armed forces serve our country (good, well).

9. Sleep (good, well) tonight, Brad.

10. We saw a (good, well) movie on cable television.

B. Complete each sentence with *good* or *well.*

1. How _____ you swim, Lisa!

2. She does a _____ deed every day.

3. My mother sews _____ .

4. Is Larry a _____ cook?

5. To be in competition, you must ski _____ .

6. You can be sure that a _____ pitcher will open the game.

7. Can you run _____ enough to join the team?

8. You danced _____ in the show.

9. I slept _____ last night.

10. This is a _____ apple.

11. Choose your friends _____ .

Their and There

Exercise 75

> *Their* is an adjective and shows possession or ownership. It is followed by the noun it modifies.
>
> *There* is an adverb and means *in that place*. *There* is sometimes used as an introductory word.

A. Complete each sentence with *their* or *there*.

1. The trees shed _____ leaves each fall.

2. Stand _____ near the gate and wait for me.

3. _____ are seven days in a week.

4. Have you seen _____ new house?

5. Many people have given _____ lives for our country.

6. _____ go my friends, Pam and Sam.

7. _____ books lay on the kitchen table.

8. _____ are millions of different fish in the sea.

9. Everyone should brush _____ teeth daily.

10. _____ are several different kinds of clouds.

11. Please place the dishes _____ .

12. Have they found _____ bicycles?

B. Circle the correct word in parentheses.

1. Many children carry (their, there) lunches to school.

2. The beavers have built (their, there) dam across the stream.

3. (Their, There) are two kinds of nouns: proper and common.

4. Our family has made several trips (their, there).

5. The campers cooked (their, there) breakfast on the open fire.

6. (Their, There) are many countries whose people live in poverty.

7. (Their, There) are thirteen doughnuts in a baker's dozen.

8. What was the cost of repairing (their, there) car?

9. (Their, There) were thirteen original American colonies.

10. The principal usually parks her car (their, there).

Real and *Very*

> *Real* is an adjective and means *genuine* or *true*.
> *Very* is an adverb and means *extremely* or *to a high degree*.

A. Complete each sentence with *real* or *very*.

1. Those people are _____ neighbors.

2. I am _____ sorry that I forgot your birthday.

3. That is a _____ good design that you drew.

4. Is your bracelet made of _____ gold?

5. A _____ happy puppy met us at the door.

6. Our family had a _____ good time at Riverside Park.

7. Are those flowers _____ or artificial?

8. The top of our coffee table is _____ marble.

9. The child stood _____ close to the curb.

10. The bride's dress is made of _____ silk.

11. My grandparents are _____ good to me.

12. The movie star's coat is _____ mink.

B. Circle the correct word in parentheses.

1. That stuffed owl looks (real, very) to me.

2. A plantation is a (real, very) large farm.

3. The movie lasted a (real, very) long time.

4. Uncle Dan caught a (real, very) shark.

5. The trapper caught a (real, very) large rabbit.

6. Colonial homes were often (real, very) cold.

7. Transportation in colonial days was (real, very) slow.

8. Rayon is often used instead of (real, very) silk.

9. A (real, very) diamond was found in our backyard.

10. The courier carried a (real, very) important message to the president.

Name _____

Two, Too, and To

> **Two** is an adjective and refers to the number 2.
>
> **Too** is an adverb and means *also, more than enough,* or *besides.*
>
> **To** is a preposition. It is usually used to indicate motion toward some place, person, or thing.

A. Complete each sentence with *two, too,* or *to.*

1. In the United States there are _____ major mountain ranges.

2. I ran _____ school when I heard the bell.

3. We cannot be _____ thoughtful of others.

4. Our new home is _____ miles west of the city.

5. Many Spanish missionaries came _____ the New World.

6. I was sick in bed for _____ days last week.

7. That table is _____ high to use for typing.

8. We are going _____ the beach for vacation this year.

9. _____ huge elephants led the parade.

10. _____ much candy is not good for you.

11. Do not stand _____ near the curb.

12. Oranges and grapefruits are _____ citrus fruits.

B. Circle the correct word in parentheses.

1. I like carrots, but I like spinach (two, too, to).

2. The farmer must take his vegetables (two, too, to) market.

3. Are there (two, too, to) pencils on your desk?

4. The storm warning came (two, too, to) late to save the town.

5. Columbus made four voyages (two, too, to) America.

6. Our ancestors came from a town (two, too, to) miles from Limerick.

7. Do not sit (two, too, to) close to the television.

8. Can you name (two, too, to) great composers?

9. Cotton and wool are (two, too, to) important textiles.

10. The explorers climbed (two, too, to) the top of the mountain.

No, Not, and *Never*

Exercise 78

> A negative idea is expressed by using *one* negative word. This negative may be *no, not, never,* or *nothing.* These words should be used only in sentences that have no other negative word.

A. Circle the correct word in parentheses.

1. None of my friends has (ever, never) seen a farm.

2. There isn't (any, no) water on the table.

3. I have (ever, never) ridden in an airplane.

4. There were (any, no) girls in the pool.

5. She didn't ask (any, no) questions.

6. I can't hear (any, no) noise.

7. We haven't bought (any, no) cookies.

8. Aren't there (any, no) apples left?

9. Don't you know (any, no) jokes?

10. Haven't you (ever, never) visited an amusement park?

11. The picnickers had (any, no) food left.

12. I have (ever, never) been on a ship before now.

B. Complete each sentence to express a negative idea.

1. Bill hasn't _____ work to do.

2. Weren't you _____ in this museum before?

3. I have _____ read an Edgar Allan Poe mystery.

4. Didn't you bring _____ lunch with you?

5. This puppy hasn't _____ collar.

6. There was _____ address on this envelope.

7. Vince has _____ been to the mountains.

8. This test paper hasn't _____ name at the top.

9. My watch hasn't _____ minute hand.

10. This lost kitten hasn't _____ identification.

11. Julie hasn't _____ been skiing before.

Review of Adverbs

Exercise 79

Write on the line whether the italicized adverb is an adverb of time, place, or manner.

_____ 1. After being tossed by the wind, the kite crashed *down*.

_____ 2. We received a telegram from my uncle *yesterday*.

_____ 3. The hungry campers ate their breakfast *heartily*.

_____ 4. Our family goes out for breakfast *often*.

_____ 5. At the mother bird's call, the baby birds flew *away*.

_____ 6. Talented Tina does all things *well*.

_____ 7. *Finally*, the game was over!

_____ 8. After an unsure takeoff, the plane soared *high*.

_____ 9. The rabbit darted *swiftly* through the trees.

_____ 10. *Gracefully*, the ballerina tiptoed across the stage.

Complete the chart with the comparative and superlative degree of each adverb.

	comparative	superlative
11. well	_____	_____
12. faithfully	_____	_____
13. badly	_____	_____
14. high	_____	_____
15. far	_____	_____

Write on the line whether the italicized adverb is in the
P—positive, **C**—comparative, or **S**—superlative degree.

_____ 16. Scott is feeling *better* today.

_____ 17. The boat glided *smoothly* over the water.

_____ 18. Missy swam *best* of all the swimmers.

_____ 19. My dog *faithfully* brings me the paper from the porch.

_____ 20. I study *more diligently* for science tests than for social studies tests.

Review of Adverbs

Circle the correct word in parentheses.

21. This bathing suit is (two, too, to) large for me.

22. I have (ever, never) ridden in a subway train.

23. Danny and Russ carved (their, there) initials in a bar of soap.

24. (Two, Too, To) more days and it will be my birthday!

25. I am reading a (very, real) good adventure story.

26. These are (very, real) Spanish coins.

27. We couldn't find (no, any) arrowheads on our hike.

28. Keith can ride a skateboard (good, well).

29. The coins in this collection are (real, very) old.

30. (Their, There) are the flowers that I planted last year.

31. Larry swam (to, too) the end of the pool and back again.

32. Keep the (good, well) potatoes for the salad.

33. Andy didn't want (any, no) tapioca.

34. Over (their, there) are the (two, to) new holly bushes.

35. The puppy's nose is cold so he must be (good, well).

Prepositions and Prepositional Phrases

Exercise 80

A preposition is a word placed before a noun or a pronoun. The noun or pronoun is called the object of the preposition.

Here are some common prepositions.

about	around	before	down	from	of	through	up
above	against	beside	during	in	off	to	with
across	among	between	except	into	on	toward	
after	at	by	for	near	over	under	

A. Circle the prepositions in each sentence.

1. Bicycle riding is fun (for) all ages.

2. Some adults ride bicycles to work every day.

3. Mothers take their small children for rides in the park.

4. Many children ride bicycles to school.

5. Bicycles come in all shapes and sizes.

6. There are small bicycles with training wheels for use on sidewalks.

7. There are also multispeed bicycles for racing on streets.

8. The gears of multispeed bicycles make pedaling easier.

9. When going up a hill, the rider shifts into low gear.

10. The rider uses high gear on level surfaces.

B. Circle the preposition and underline the prepositional phrase in each sentence.

1. The tree near the garage is maple.

2. The house across the street has been sold.

3. What is that leaning against the chalkboard?

4. In a week my Uncle Matt may return.

5. I cannot see through these glasses.

6. A small crowd came toward the speaker.

7. The baby crawled slowly up the stairs.

8. Above the clouds the airplane soared.

9. Serious athletes jogged around the track.

10. Everybody has gone except Patty.

Writing Prepositions

Exercise 81

A. Complete each sentence with an appropriate preposition.

1. _____ November we celebrate Thanksgiving.

2. He tiptoed _____ the room.

3. My parents have gone _____ the meeting.

4. Carol went _____ the haunted house.

5. Robert coasted _____ the hill.

6. Don't fall_____ that ladder, Cindy.

7. Is your mother_____ home?

8. The frightened kitten hid _____ the huge box.

9. Pull the warm blanket_____ you.

10. We fished _____ the New Jersey shore.

11. We enjoyed ourselves _____ the swimming pool.

12. Rick slid _____ home plate.

13. The United States imports coffee _____ Brazil.

14. Walk _____ us, Tanya.

15. The exhausted rescuers trudged _____ the snow.

B. Complete each sentence with a prepositional phrase.

1. The baby crept ____ across the floor. _____

2. The astronauts landed _____

3. The young girl stood _____

4. Uncle Mark sits _____

5. Julia brought a box _____

6. Susan splashed water _____

7. Everybody has gone _____

8. Our baby cannot walk _____

9. May I carry the package _____

10. The telephone was invented _____

Between and Among

Exercise 82

> Use *between* in speaking of two persons or objects. Use *among* in speaking of more than two persons or objects.

A. Circle the correct preposition in parentheses.

1. Amy walked (between, among) her two sisters.

2. The United States lies (between, among) the Atlantic and the Pacific oceans.

3. Distribute the papers (between, among) the students in the class.

4. A beautiful flower grew (between, among) the weeds.

5. The band marched (between, among) two lines of spectators.

6. The two boys carried the injured man (between, among) them.

7. A lasting friendship exists (between, among) the United States and Canada.

8. Is that a secret (between, among) the two of you?

9. Our airplane is (between, among) those on the runway.

10. You may sit (between, among) Jay and me.

11. Alabama is (between, among) Georgia and Mississippi.

12. Our leaders work for peace (between, among) all the nations of the world.

13. Share the fruit (between, among) the four of you.

14. The flower arrangement sat (between, among) two candles.

B. Complete each sentence with *between* or *among*.

1. Those five boys often quarrel _____ themselves.

2. Trade is carried on _____ North and South America.

3. There isn't one tall player _____ the five.

4. _____ you and me, whom shall we choose?

5. The awards were divided _____ the three top winners.

6. There is a joyful spirit _____ the students in our class.

7. The garage stands _____ the house and the barn.

8. There was one stranger _____ the four visitors.

9. _____ them, the two brothers made the model ship.

10. May I walk _____ Ron and you?

From and *Off*

Exercise 83

> Use *from* in speaking of a person from whom something is received. Use *off* to mean *away from*. The expression *off of* is never correct.

A. Circle the correct preposition in parentheses.

1. Be careful or you will fall (from, off) that chair.

2. When you enter the room, take your hat (from, off).

3. We bought corn (from, off) the farmer.

4. She swept the leaves (off of, off) the porch.

5. (From, Off) whom did you receive that interesting book?

6. Take the message (from, off) him, please.

7. Who slid (off of, off) the seat?

8. Her pen rolled (from, off) her desk onto the floor.

9. These skates are a gift (from, off) my uncle.

10. My mother orders her books (from, off) this catalog.

11. The boy hopped (from, off) his bicycle.

12. This watch is a present (from, off) my grandparents.

13. The puppy knocked the decorations (from, off) the tree.

B. Complete each sentence with *from* or *off*.

1. Don't jump _____ the step.

2. We obtain peanuts _____ Georgia.

3. The farmer hopped _____ the tractor.

4. My mother buys delicious cakes _____ that bakery.

5. I get interesting books _____ our library.

6. The sign read, "Keep _____ the grass."

7. The lid fell _____ the tin can.

8. Kevin stepped _____ the train quickly.

9. I learned how to print _____ my teacher.

10. You may get a paper _____ the shelf in the closet.

Recognizing Adjectival Phrases

Exercise 84

An adjectival phrase is used as an adjective. It contains a preposition and an object.

A. Underline the adjectival phrase in each sentence. Write on the line the noun each adjectival phrase modifies.

_____flowers_____ 1. The flowers on the desk are roses.

_____ 2. The ship from France has docked.

_____ 3. The dog with the shiny coat won the prize.

_____ 4. The tree near the house fell.

_____ 5. Homes in early colonial days had no windowpanes.

_____ 6. The orchestra played the music of famous composers.

_____ 7. The rescuers performed many acts of courage.

_____ 8. That large store in the mall sells sporting goods.

_____ 9. A woman with a kind expression directed us.

_____ 10. The people in that house speak Spanish.

_____ 11. The berries on that bush are ripe.

_____ 12. Every hour the clock on the mantle chimes.

_____ 13. The Liberty Bell announced the birth of a new nation.

B. Underline the adjectival phrases in the paragraph. Circle the noun each phrase modifies.

Are you a person with hay fever? Hay fever is an allergy with definite symptoms. All seasons except winter are bad times for sufferers. This allergy produces uncomfortable irritations in the eyes, nose, and throat. The eyes of the victim may become red, itchy, and watery. The nose with its swollen membrane may itch and run. The throat with its sensitivity becomes prey, too. "What is the cause of all this grief?" you ask. Pollen from plants is the culprit! If you endure the symptoms of this annoying condition, seek help. Your doctor can supply a remedy from a long list of medications.

Writing Adjectival Phrases

Rewrite each sentence, changing the italicized adjective to an adjectival phrase.

1. I prefer a *ham and cheese* sandwich.

   _____

2. The *mountain* cabin was evacuated before the flood.

   _____

3. The *team* captain will retire at the end of the season.

   _____

4. That *flower* garden looks magnificent.

   _____

5. The *wooden* rocker creaked on the porch.

   _____

6. *Iron* fences often get rusty.

   _____

7. The *fruit* basket was delivered to the hospital.

   _____

8. The *grounded* plane awaited repairs.

   _____

9. The third little pig built a *brick* house.

   _____

10. This store sells *New Jersey* produce.

    _____

11. That ship carries *Brazilian* coffee.

    _____

Recognizing Adverbial Phrases

Exercise 86

| An adverbial phrase is used as an adverb. It contains a preposition and an object. |

A. Underline the adverbial phrase in each sentence. Write on the line the verb each adverbial phrase modifies.

_____pointed_____ 1. Brady pointed to the map.

_____ 2. The sheriff's horse clattered up the rocky trail.

_____ 3. Her eyes flashed with excitement.

_____ 4. This road turns to the east.

_____ 5. Through the meadow the stream flows.

_____ 6. We traveled by airplane.

_____ 7. Down the Delaware River Terry rafted.

_____ 8. Sugarcane grows in a warm, moist climate.

_____ 9. Coffee beans are dried in the hot sun.

_____ 10. The rabbits disappeared over the hill.

_____ 11. Roger's family moved into a new house.

B. Complete each sentence with an adverbial phrase.

1. The railroad winds _____

2. We traveled _____

3. The injured boy stumbled _____

4. The hiker gazed _____

5. Rain trickled _____

6. The couple sauntered _____

7. My aunt lives _____

8. The jogger ran _____

9. The baby crawled _____

10. The kite soared _____

Writing Adverbial Phrases

Rewrite each sentence, changing the italicized adverb to an adverbial phrase.

1. The carpenter handles his tools *carefully*.

   _____

2. The soldiers saluted their commanding officer *respectfully*.

   _____

3. The dog barked *angrily* at the stranger.

   _____

4. Our team shouted *joyfully* when we won.

   _____

5. The kitten purred *contentedly* in the corner.

   _____

6. The teacher smiled *approvingly* at the student.

   _____

7. The jazz dancer performed *gracefully*.

   _____

8. Janet learns math *easily*.

   _____

9. The mother looked *lovingly* at the baby.

   _____

10. The surgeon operated *skillfully* on the patient.

   _____

11. The student answered *intelligently*.

   _____

Distinguishing between Adjectival and Adverbial Phrases

Exercise 88

A. Underline the prepositional phrase in each sentence. Write on the line whether it is adjectival or adverbial.

_____ 1. The earth revolves around the sun.

_____ 2. A storm destroyed the flowers in our garden.

_____ 3. The clerk in the store helped us.

_____ 4. The dog ran under the porch.

_____ 5. Tommy washed his hands at the kitchen sink.

_____ 6. The Ohio River flows into the Mississippi.

_____ 7. The fire in the garage caused great damage.

_____ 8. Ellie tucked the package under her arm.

_____ 9. The rays of the sun can be harmful.

_____ 10. Bananas grow in a warm climate.

_____ 11. Volunteers from our block cleaned the vacant lot.

_____ 12. A helicopter flew over the school.

_____ 13. The cookies in that jar are homemade.

_____ 14. The fur of the rabbit was soft and white.

_____ 15. The golf course was built along the coast.

B. Complete each sentence with an adjectival and adverbial phrase.

1. The flowers _____ were grown _____

2. The balloons _____ were bought _____

3. The clock _____ chimes _____

4. The bike _____ was hit _____

5. The baseball game _____ was won _____

6. The kite _____ flew _____

Name

Conjunctions Connecting Subjects

Exercise 89

A conjunction is a word that connects words or groups of words. The most common conjunctions are *and, or,* and *but.* A compound subject is connected by a conjunction.

A. Circle the conjunction in each sentence. Underline the subjects it connects.

1. The students *and* teachers entered the auditorium.

2. The United States and Europe are in the Northern Hemisphere.

3. Marquette and La Salle explored the Mississippi River.

4. Tulips or daffodils will look nice in this flower arrangement.

5. The bat and glove belong to me.

6. President Kennedy and Robert Kennedy were brothers.

7. Brothers and sisters should care for one another.

8. The actors and director have just arrived.

9. Asia and Africa are the two largest continents.

10. Not apples but peaches froze on these trees.

B. Complete each sentence with a conjunction to connect the subjects.

1. Meg _____ Tina play together.

2. He _____ I will go to the store for you.

3. Clarinets _____ oboes are woodwind instruments.

4. California _____ Oregon border the Pacific Ocean.

5. England _____ France claimed the Ohio Valley.

C. Complete each sentence with a compound subject.

1. _____ and _____ eat corn.

2. Not _____ but _____ heard the noise.

3. _____ and _____ are winter months.

4. _____ and _____ enhanced the celebration.

5. Either _____ or _____ accompanied the choir.

6. _____ or _____ will assist you.

Conjunctions Connecting Predicates

Exercise 90

> A conjunction is a word that connects words or groups of words. The most common conjunctions are *and, or,* and *but.* A compound predicate is connected by a conjunction.

A. Circle the conjunction in each sentence. Underline the predicates it connects.

1. My little brother reads and writes well.

2. We must either sweep or mop the floor, Martha.

3. We stopped and watched the sunset.

4. The excited fans cheered and applauded the team.

5. The tired farmer stopped and rested in the field.

6. Greg sneezed and shivered from the cold.

7. The doctor examined and tested the patient.

8. The guard dog either stares or yawns at strangers.

9. The teacher marked and graded the tests.

10. The car squealed and stopped just in time.

B. Complete each sentence with a conjunction to connect the predicates.

1. Grapes are squeezed _____ crushed to make grape juice.

2. The hunter shot _____ killed the bear.

3. I bent _____ peeked through the hole in the fence.

4. The frightened deer either hid _____ dashed away.

5. The clown juggled _____ tumbled in the show.

C. Complete each sentence with a compound predicate.

1. The audience_____ and _____ for the speaker.

2. The old car _____ and _____ .

3. The plane _____ and _____ on the runway.

4. The puppy _____ and _____ when I arrive.

5. Everybody either _____ or _____ at the party.

6. Rick _____ and _____ the letter.

7. The twins _____ and _____ the dishes.

Conjunctions Connecting Direct Objects

Exercise 91

A conjunction is a word that connects words or groups of words. The most common conjunctions are *and, or,* and *but.* A compound direct object is connected by a conjunction.

A. Circle the conjunction in each sentence. Underline the direct objects it connects.

1. Einstein practiced patience and perseverance.

2. Mexico produces gold and silver.

3. The poor children had no breakfast or lunch.

4. Farmers in the Midwest raise corn and beans.

5. Our bakery makes delicious pies and cakes.

6. You may use a pencil or pen for the test.

7. Airplanes transport mail and passengers.

8. Ranchers in the West raise cattle and hogs.

9. Around the house he planted trees and shrubs.

10. Serve Mother or Grandmother first.

B. Complete each sentence with a conjunction to connect the direct objects.

1. Have you lost this pen _____ pencil?

2. I have not seen either Jean _____ her sister.

3. They did not insure either their house _____ their furniture.

4. Our music teacher plays the piano _____ the violin.

5. Emily washed her face _____ hands before dinner.

C. Complete each sentence with a compound direct object.

1. Please close the _____ and _____ .

2. The waiter served _____ and _____ for dessert.

3. We saw the _____ and _____ through the telescope.

4. I have a _____ and _____ for pets.

5. Rob studies either _____ or _____ every night.

6. The artist mixed _____ and _____ to make orange.

7. Julie bought _____ and _____ for the party.

Conjunctions Connecting Sentences

Exercise 92

> A conjunction is a word that connects words or groups of words. The most common conjunctions are *and, or,* and *but.* Sentences are connected by a conjunction.

A. Add a conjunction to connect the two sentences. Use *and, but,* or *or.* In some sentences, more than one conjunction may be correct.

1. You must study every night, _____ you may do poorly in school.

2. We went to meet the plane, _____ it didn't arrive on time.

3. The storm lasted through the night, _____ it caused much damage.

4. Some dinosaurs ate meat, _____ others ate plants.

5. Our family went to the shore for vacation, _____ it rained every day.

6. I went to the mall on Saturday, _____ I met my friend there.

7. Cindy likes chocolate sundaes, _____ I prefer butterscotch.

8. Brush your teeth after every meal, _____ you may develop cavities.

9. Diamonds are precious gems, _____ they are also used for industry.

10. Last year we went to Florida, _____ this year we are going to Arizona.

B. Circle the conjunction in each sentence and underline the words it connects. Write on the line whether the conjunction connects subjects, predicates, direct objects, or sentences.

_____ 1. Our class art project on color required paint and water.

_____ 2. First, we filled the jars and glasses with water.

_____ 3. Next, we gathered paints and brushes together.

_____ 4. Color wheels and charts were hung around the room.

_____ 5. Then, the boys and girls had a contest.

_____ 6. Trudy mixed blue and yellow to make green.

_____ 7. Next, Ted tried red and blue.

_____ 8. He mixed and blended the colors to get violet.

_____ 9. Tara mixed red and green together.

_____ 10. It didn't look like a color, but it looked more like mud!

Interjections

An interjection expresses a strong feeling or emotion. Listed below are some common interjections.

joy—*Hurrah! Bravo! Great! Oh!*   wonder—*Ah! Oh!*
disgust—*Oh! Ick! Yuck!*   sorrow—*Oh! Ah!*
caution—*Hush! Shh! Uh-oh!*   greeting—*Hello!*
pain—*Oh! Ouch!*   surprise—*What! Oh! Aha! Wow!*

A. Underline the interjection in each sentence. Write on the line what emotion it expresses.

_____ 1. Oh! I just stepped in a puddle.

_____ 2. Yuck! I just stepped in chewing gum.

_____ 3. Oh! I have forgotten my wallet.

_____ 4. What! Has she returned so soon?

_____ 5. Ouch! I just cut my finger.

_____ 6. I think I hear a noise outside. Shh!

_____ 7. Oh! My goldfish has died.

_____ 8. Ick! I have ice cream on my shirt.

_____ 9. Wow! That's a beautiful picture.

_____ 10. You did a wonderful job. Bravo!

B. Complete each sentence with an interjection.

1. _____ Have you been here long?

2. _____ Try again.

3. _____ You can't lift the box without help.

4. The play has started. _____

5. _____ What was that noise?

6. _____ You have done well.

7. _____ The baby bird has fallen from the nest.

8. _____ That hurt.

9. _____ We have missed the train.

Review of Prepositions, Conjunctions, and Interjections

Exercise 94

Circle the preposition in each sentence. Underline the prepositional phrase.

1. The dog jumped over the fence.

2. The book on the shelf is a dictionary.

3. The window was left open during the storm.

4. Inside the box I found my old shoe.

5. Sit on the porch with me.

Circle the correct preposition in parentheses.

6. The shirts were distributed (between, among) the members of the team.

7. Just (between, among) you and me, I don't like them.

8. Their color is somewhere (between, among) green and yellow.

9. We bought them (from, off) a dealer for a reduced price.

10. As soon as I take mine (from, off), I'm trading it in for a new one.

Write on the line whether each italicized phrase is adjectival or adverbial.

The tree (11) *on the hill* was struck (12) *by lightning.* The mishap occurred

(13) *during a violent storm.* It was a hot day (14) *in August.* The dark clouds rolled

(15) *across the sky.* Raindrops (16) *of enormous size* pelted the countryside.

Thunder echoed (17) *with loud booms* and lightning darted (18) *across the heavens.*

It only lasted (19) *for a short time.* Then, the dark clouds were replaced (20) *by a*

blue sky.

11. _____   16. _____

12. _____   17. _____

13. _____   18. _____

14. _____   19. _____

15. _____   20. _____

Review of Prepositions, Conjunctions, and Interjections

Exercise 94, continued

Write on the line whether the italicized conjunction connects subjects, predicates, direct objects, or sentences.

_____ 21. Violins *and* violas are stringed instruments.

_____ 22. Cellos *and* basses also belong to the string family.

_____ 23. You pluck *or* bow these instruments to produce the sound.

_____ 24. Each instrument produces a different tone *or* quality.

_____ 25. Catgut *and* steel are the materials from which the string are made.

_____ 26. The body *and* neck of the instrument are made from a special wood.

_____ 27. A horsehair bow is gently pulled *and* pushed over the strings.

_____ 28. In an orchestra, the strings carry *and* sustain the melody.

_____ 29. Their range *and* tone allow them to be used for many parts.

_____ 30. Each string instrument is beautiful, *but* together their sound is unequaled.

Complete each sentence with an interjection.

31. _____ ! Is anybody in there?

32. I spilled the ink. _____ !

33. _____ ! That stove is hot.

34. _____ ! I'm so proud of you, Brian.

35. _____ ! What a surprise.

Review of Parts of Speech

Exercise 95

A. Write on the line the part of speech of each italicized word.

noun	**pronoun**	**verb**	**adjective**
adverb	**preposition**	**conjunction**	**interjection**

_____ 1. Did you know that not all *monkeys* have tails?

_____ 2. We knew *he* won the election before the ballots were in.

_____ 3. *Wow!* That was a scary ride.

_____ 4. The baby chameleon crawled *across* the sunny rock.

_____ 5. A *delicate* spider web clung to the branch.

_____ 6. We made jelly *and* jam from the fruit trees in our yard.

_____ 7. *Yesterday,* Clare bought a suncatcher for her window.

_____ 8. *Great!* My poem is posted on the bulletin board.

_____ 9. Does the Great Salt Lake *really* have salt in it?

_____ 10. The rabbit waited before he *attacked* the lettuce.

B. Complete each sentence with the part of speech indicated.

adverb　　　　1. Pam ran _____ into the house to call the fire department.

verb　　　　2. The small black snake _____ under the leaves.

preposition　　3. _____ the gates came a strange looking man in a costume.

adjective　　4. _____ vegetables were on the counter in the kitchen.

interjection　5. _____! I got his autograph.

pronoun　　6. Judy took _____ to the mountains with her.

noun　　　　7. A _____ wandered right up to our front door.

adjective　　8. These pears are sweet and _____ .

conjunction　9. Can you rub your stomach _____ pat your head at the same time?

verb　　　　10. Mark _____ through the woods with a heavy backpack.

Subject and Predicate

Exercise 96

> The subject names a person, a place, or a thing about which a statement is made.
> The predicate tells something about the subject.

A. Write on the lines the simple subject and simple predicate of each sentence.

	subject	predicate
1. A little boat skimmed across the lake.		
2. Several students worked on the project.		
3. Excited children danced at the party.		
4. Dry leaves whirled silently in the fall air.		
5. The guard dog barked loudly at the stranger.		
6. The tall ships sailed gracefully into the harbor.		
7. Experienced swimmers competed in the relay.		
8. The circus tigers roared ferociously.		
9. Colorful flowers bloom in our garden.		
10. Soft snow fell steadily through the night.		
11. The courageous girl dived into the pool.		
12. Many persons exercise in this spa.		

B. Complete each sentence with a subject or a predicate.

1. Our _____ won the championship this year.

2. Birds _____ south for the winter.

3. The weary travelers _____ in the shade.

4. Rudy _____ the lyrics to this song.

5. The _____ crept through the old mansion.

6. Snow _____ silently over the town.

7. The _____ came to a sudden stop.

8. Lightning _____ many people.

9. The storm _____ the telephones wires.

10. The hikers _____ home after a long day.

The Complete Subject

Exercise 97

> **The subject with all its modifiers is called the complete subject.**

A. Circle the simple subject and underline the complete subject in each sentence.

1. Dark, heavy clouds gathered overhead.

2. The frightened little mouse ran under the cabinet.

3. A large green truck passed the house.

4. The carefree boy whistled a tune.

5. The faithful messenger delivered the letter.

6. The circus seals played in the water.

7. The trained juggler performed for the audience.

8. The great iron bell tolled in the tower.

9. The new student answered the question correctly.

10. Two heavy trucks collided at the corner.

11. The thick fog has lifted.

12. Many valuable trees grow in our state.

B. Complete each sentence with descriptive adjectives or adjectival phrases. Put parentheses around the complete subject.

1. Aren't _____ flowers lovely?

2. _____ canoes glided downstream.

3. The engine _____ chugged and sputtered.

4. _____ squirrels chattered and played.

5. The athlete _____ won the competition.

6. The people _____ cheered for the hometown team.

7. The _____ tree _____ fell during the storm.

8. The ice _____ has thawed.

9. The _____ snake slithered down the hole.

10. The _____ kitten _____ purred with delight.

The Complete Predicate

Exercise 98

> The predicate with all its modifiers, objects, and complements is called the complete predicate.

A. Circle the simple predicate and underline the complete predicate in each sentence.

1. We (visited) the busy factory.

2. Donkeys carry heavy loads up the mountain trails.

3. The swimmer dived into the cold water.

4. The choir sang beautiful songs for the Easter festival.

5. Indians made colorful clay dishes.

6. We drew a map of South America in art class.

7. The building was painted light brown.

8. The vendor sold hot peanuts and cold drinks.

9. I wore my old clothes to the picnic.

10. The team carried the winning coach on their shoulders.

11. The horse galloped across the meadow and down the trail.

12. The family built a log cabin in the mountains.

B. Complete each sentence with modifiers, objects, or complements. Put parentheses around the complete predicate.

1. Stephen was given _____

2. David ate _____

3. Carol had written _____

4. Lightning streaked _____

5. The tourists crowded _____

6. Paul told _____

7. Weeds grew _____

8. The vacationing family stopped _____

9. The spotted terrier bounded _____

10. The pilot climbed _____

Sentence Sense

Exercise 99

A sentence is a group of words that expresses a complete thought. Every sentence has a subject and a predicate.

A. Write **complete** on the line if the words form a sentence.
    Write **incomplete** on the line if the words do not form a sentence.

_____ 1. I'm interested in electronics.

_____ 2. The rough muddy road.

_____ 3. Pony Express riders carried mail.

_____ 4. The game starts in ten minutes.

_____ 5. The athlete threw the javelin through the air.

_____ 6. Ponce de León discovered Florida.

_____ 7. The envelope on the desk.

_____ 8. Early in the morning.

_____ 9. The pioneers traveled in covered wagons.

_____ 10. Many years ago.

_____ 11. Mules provided transportation in the deserts.

_____ 12. The navigator guided the ship through the channel.

B. Rewrite each incomplete sentence to make a complete sentence. The first letter of each group of words should not be capitalized unless it begins the sentence.

the heavy door   1._____

the agile runner   2._____

the flat tire   3._____

when it rains   4._____

on the mountain   5._____

a big black cat   6._____

around the corner   7._____

gets better each day 8._____

Compound Subjects

Exercise 100

If the subject of a sentence has more than one noun or pronoun, it is said to be a compound subject.

A. Underline the compound subject in each sentence. Circle the conjunction.

1. The sun and moon give light.

2. Cows and sheep eat plants.

3. Kings and queens rule in a monarchy.

4. Grapes and peaches grow on that farm.

5. Brian and Patty swept the kitchen floor.

6. Buffalo and Rochester are important manufacturing cities.

7. The actors and actresses entered the auditorium.

8. Fruits and vegetables are a good source of vitamins.

9. Yesterday, Rick and Dave fed apples to the horses.

10. Each year, hunger and sickness cause many deaths.

11. Jim and his father are lawyers.

12. The doctor and nurse have arrived at the clinic.

B. Complete each sentence with a compound subject.

1. _____ and _____ have gone to the mall.

2. Will _____ and _____ be coming to visit us?

3. _____ and _____ made a sand castle.

4. _____ and _____ season food.

5. In the armed forces _____ and _____ have protected our freedom.

6. _____ and _____ enjoy tennis in the summer.

7. Do _____ and _____ use that road?

8. _____ and _____ are good team sports.

9. Can _____ and _____ live together in the same tank?

10. _____ and _____ are my favorite games.

Name _____

Compound Predicates

Exercise 101

If the predicate of a sentence is made up of more than one verb, it is said to be a compound predicate.

A. Underline the compound predicate in each sentence. Circle the conjunction.

1. The crowd waved and cheered at the team.

2. Will you swim or dive for our school team?

3. The chairperson rose and spoke to the committee.

4. The plane's engines whined and whistled before takeoff.

5. The patients sat and waited for the doctor.

6. You can either print or write your name.

7. Busy workers came and went through the factory doors.

8. The doors opened and closed frequently.

9. The baby walks and talks well.

10. The children laughed and shouted as they played.

11. The bunny hopped and jumped through the grass.

12. The teachers sat and talked at the meeting.

B. Combine each pair of sentences into one sentence with a compound predicate.

1. The judge heard the case. The judge ruled on the case.

_____

2. After you study close your book. After you study answer the questions.

_____

3. Ellie found the expensive ring. Ellie returned the ring to its owner.

_____

4. Before the storm Peggy shut the window. Before the storm Peggy locked the window.

_____

Compound Objects

Exercise 102

> If the direct object of a verb has more than one noun or pronoun, it is said to be a compound object.

A. Underline the compound object in each sentence. Circle the conjunction.

1. I prefer fruit or sherbet for dessert.

2. The farmer planted corn and wheat in the field.

3. Hawaii exports sugarcane and pineapple.

4. I bought a dictionary and some notebooks.

5. Ask Michael or him about it.

6. He won a new boat and a car in the contest.

7. My mother bakes delicious pies and cakes.

8. The president visited New York and Chicago.

9. Wear your scarf and gloves, children.

10. Kevin caught some trout and bluefish yesterday.

11. My sister lost her wallet and her watch.

12. Write your name and address on the ticket.

13. He drives a car or motorcycle to work.

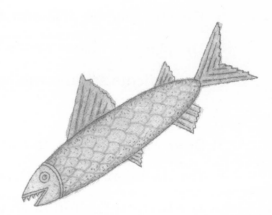

B. Complete each sentence with a compound object.

1. I drove _____ and _____ to the airport.

2. Do you have a _____ or a _____ ?

3. Irene wanted a new _____ or _____ for her birthday.

4. The Indians brought _____ and _____ to the first Thanksgiving.

5. All living things need _____ and _____ .

6. The waitress served us _____ and _____ for lunch.

7. I found _____ and _____ on the beach.

8. My brother collects _____ and _____ as a hobby.

9. The doctor prescribed _____ and _____ for the patient.

10. I like a _____ or _____ for a pet.

Review of Compound Elements in a Sentence

Exercise 103

A. Underline the compound element in each sentence. Write on the line whether it is a compound subject, predicate, or direct object.

_____ 1. The snow and sleet fell during the night.

_____ 2. Fields and woods glistened like diamonds.

_____ 3. Every street and road became a hazard.

_____ 4. Cars skidded and slid from side to side.

_____ 5. Some even banged and crashed into each other.

_____ 6. Schools and businesses closed for the day.

_____ 7. Dads shoveled and salted pavements.

_____ 8. Salt trucks and plows cleared the roads.

_____ 9. The weather invited teens and youngsters to play.

_____ 10. Children of all ages grabbed sleds and toboggans.

_____ 11. They ran and played in huge mounds of snow.

_____ 12. They built snowmen and snow forts.

_____ 13. Snowballs whizzed and spun through the air.

_____ 14. Adults and children were happy at the end of the day.

B. Write sentences using each compound element.

jumped and played 1. _____

Molly and Jeff 2. _____

burgers and fries 3. _____

thunder and lightning 4. _____

wrote and mailed 5. _____

screamed and hollered 6. _____

Natural and Inverted Order in Sentences

Exercise 104

> Whenever the complete predicate follows the complete subject, the sentence is in the natural order.
>
> Whenever the complete predicate or part of the predicate is placed before the subject, the sentence is in the inverted order.

A. Underline the simple subject and circle the simple predicate. Write **N** if the sentence is in the natural order and **I** if the sentence is in the inverted order.

_____ 1. The spaceship soared onward.

_____ 2. Diaz sailed around Africa.

_____ 3. Westward sailed the ship.

_____ 4. The car bounced up and down over the bumps.

_____ 5. The mayor has never been to Atlanta, Georgia.

_____ 6. The sun shone through the clouds.

_____ 7. Fresh fruit filled the basket.

_____ 8. The early settlers raised corn.

_____ 9. Across the pool swam Chuck.

_____ 10. Their friends have moved to another town.

_____ 11. The sailor paced the deck.

_____ 12. Up stepped the small boy.

B. Rewrite each sentence in the inverted order. The complete predicate is italicized.

1. Beautifully carved figures _decorated the hallways in the mansion._

_____

2. The tiger _darted behind the tree._

_____

3. A beautiful Christmas wreath _hung on the front door._

_____

Kinds of Sentences

Exercise 105

> There are four kinds of sentences: declarative, interrogative, imperative, and exclamatory.
>
> A declarative sentence states a fact. An interrogative sentence asks a question.
>
> An imperative sentence gives a command. An exclamatory sentence expresses strong emotion.

A. Write on the line whether each sentence is declarative, interrogative, imperative, or exclamatory.

_____ 1. Many people go to the mall every day.

_____ 2. Is this your math book?

_____ 3. Name the chief cities of Greece.

_____ 4. How courageous the police officer was!

_____ 5. Have you ever used a felt-tipped pen?

_____ 6. Keep to the right of the road.

_____ 7. Margie has a new yellow dress.

_____ 8. How difficult that problem is!

B. Add the end punctuation to each sentence. Write on the line what kind of sentence it is.

_____ 1. The first human heart transplant occurred in 1967

_____ 2. The city was decorated with lights

_____ 3. How that boy amazes me

_____ 4. Watch how I do the problem

_____ 5. There are 206 bones in the body

_____ 6. What a wonderful surprise this is

_____ 7. Have you ever read _Romona the Pest_

_____ 8. Blue is your best color

_____ 9. Where is the key for the front door

_____ 10. We are trying to save animals from extinction

Change in Sentence Form

Exercise 106

A. Rewrite each sentence in the form indicated.

1. My address is on the envelope.

   interrogative: _____

2. Did each castle in medieval times have a moat?

   declarative: _____

3. The sunset is colorful today.

   exclamatory: _____

4. Are you walking on my wet floor?

   exclamatory: _____

5. The abandoned house is haunted by ghosts.

   interrogative: _____

6. Do you brush your teeth after each meal?

   imperative: _____

7. Nancy can go to the play later.

   imperative: _____

8. This mystery book is interesting.

   exclamatory: _____

9. Do nomads roam in the Sahara Desert?

   declarative: _____

10. Is the puppy in the yard?

    declarative: _____

11. Do you like your birthday gift?

    exclamatory: _____

Name _____

Review of Sentences

Exercise 107

Write on the line whether the italicized words are the
CS—complete subject or **CP**—complete predicate.

_____ 1. *The ferocious fire-breathing dragon* descended upon the town.

_____ 2. Flames of fire *shot from its hideous mouth.*

_____ 3. Its loud roar *echoed in the night.*

_____ 4. Trees and bushes *were leveled by one swoop of its mighty tail.*

_____ 5. *Its huge feet* trampled homes flat.

_____ 6. *Sleepy townsfolk* awoke with fear.

_____ 7. Mothers *grabbed their children.*

_____ 8. Who *would slay the monster and save the town?*

Write **complete** on the line if the words form a sentence. Write **incomplete** on the
line if the words do not form a sentence.

_____ 9. Skipping through the woods on a spring morning.

_____ 10. The wolf peered from behind a tree.

_____ 11. Each flower caught Red Riding Hood's attention.

_____ 12. A large bouquet for Grandmother.

_____ 13. To Grandmother's house she went.

Underline the simple subject and circle the simple predicate.
Write **N** if the sentence is in natural order and **I** if the sentence is in inverted order.

_____ 14. Keith stepped up to the pitcher's mound.

_____ 15. From the stands, the fans cheered and waved their hands.

_____ 16. His powerful arm released the ball at top speed.

_____ 17. Into the air it spun.

_____ 18. It hit the bat with a crack.

Review of Sentences

Exercise 107, continued

Write on the line whether the sentence is declarative, interrogative, imperative, or exclamatory.

_____ 19. Sit here and wait for me.

_____ 20. Do you know what time it is?

_____ 21. Here comes that ferocious dog!

_____ 22. Thunder and lightning storms often occur in summer.

_____ 23. Be careful swimming alone.

_____ 24. Too much salt is bad for your health.

_____ 25. Do you understand this lesson?

_____ 26. Please sit down and listen.

_____ 27. Look at that gorgeous sailboat!

_____ 28. My birthday comes in March.

Write on the line whether the italicized words form a compound subject, compound predicate, or compound direct object.

_____ 29. *Fruit and cereal* is my favorite breakfast.

_____ 30. The baby *splashed and played* in the kiddie pool.

_____ 31. I bought a new *comb and brush.*

_____ 32. Many tourists visit *New York and Washington.*

_____ 33. We *strolled and chatted* leisurely through the park.

_____ 34. *Cars and buses* jammed the busy intersection.

_____ 35. Please *wrap and mail* this package.

Uses of the Period

Exercise 108

A period is used at the end of a declarative or an imperative sentence; after most abbreviations; after an initial. The metric system and the two-letter state postal abbreviations do not use a period.

A. Write the correct abbreviation for each word. Use periods where needed.

1. gallon _____

2. pound _____

3. South Dakota _____

4. before Christ _____

5. Doctor _____

6. Kentucky _____

11. centimeter _____

12. inch _____

13. October _____

14. Governor _____

15. after noon _____

16. Wednesday _____

B. Add periods where needed.

1. U S sailors went aboard the ship

2. When you mail the letter, send it to P O Box 141, New York

3. When did Mrs Abraham arrive?

4. Ave is the abbreviation for avenue

5. Ronald Reagan was president from 1981 to 1988

6. Dr F X Miner has his office on Main St

7. Do you remember what happened in A D 1789?

8. Squid, octopus, crab, etc were caught in the bay

9. Mrs P Patterson's flight arrived at 8:30 P M

10. It rained for three days straight

C. Rewrite each person's name, using initials for the underlined words.

1. Dorothy <u>Marie</u> Crabbe _____

2. <u>Marcia Elizabeth</u> Cornell _____

3. <u>Cornelius</u> Francis Smith _____

4. <u>Otis Warren Bridge</u> _____

5. Patricia <u>Barrett</u> Winters _____

The Comma in a Series and in Parts of a Letter

Exercise 109

> Commas are used to separate words in a series; after the salutation and complimentary close of a letter.

A. Add commas where needed.

1. Pianos violins and drums are musical instruments.

2. Spain France England and Holland claimed land in New York.

3. We study the addition multiplication subtraction and division of fractions.

4. Blue pink yellow and green pencils were in the pack.

5. Ellen can skate swim dive and dance.

6. Dad grew carrots lettuce radishes squash and potatoes in the garden.

7. The recipe said to shake beat stir and then boil.

8. White smooth fluffy potatoes are my favorite vegetable.

9. In the picnic basket were sandwiches cookies pretzels and lemonade.

10. Martha stretched pulled shook and twisted when she did her exercises.

11. Dear Mom and Dad

12. Your friend

13. My dear Aunt Bridget

14. Love

15. Your favorite son

B. Complete each sentence with a series of nouns, verbs, or adjectives. Add commas where needed.

1. _____ _____ and_____ are my
favorite amusements at the park.

2. I can hear my brother_____ _____ and
_____ in the shower.

3. Have you seen _____ _____ _____
and _____?

4. The colors of the flag were_____ _____ and
_____ .

The Comma with Dates and Geographical Names

Exercise 110

> Place a comma between the day of the month and the year. Place a comma after the year unless it comes at the end of the sentence. Place a comma between the name of the city and the state. Place a comma after the name of the state or country unless it comes at the end of the sentence.

A. Add commas where needed.

1. U. S. Grant was born on April 22 1822.

2. On December 16 1773 the Boston Tea Party occurred.

3. At Plymouth Massachusetts the Pilgrims celebrated the first Thanksgiving.

4. Detroit Michigan is the center of the automobile industry.

5. The United States Navy was established on October 13 1775.

6. France gave the United States the Statue of Liberty on October 28 1886.

7. The Declaration of Independence was signed in Independence Hall Philadelphia Pennsylvania.

8. My best friend Louis lives in Portland Oregon.

9. There is a house shaped like an elephant in Margate New Jersey.

10. Many pyramids still stand in El Giza Egypt.

11. Have you ever visited Amsterdam Holland?

12. On May 29 1953 Sir Edmund Hillary reached the summit of Mt. Everest.

13. On July 20 1969 Neil Armstrong collected rock samples on the moon.

14. Christopher Columbus sailed from Spain on August 3 1492.

15. The first permanent English settlement was begun in Jamestown Virginia in 1607.

B. Complete each sentence with real or imaginary information. Use correct punctuation.

1. I was born on _____

2. Sheila just returned from _____

3. On _____ earmuffs were invented.

4. Jerry rode in a hot-air balloon on _____

5. Someday I would love to visit _____

The Comma with *Yes*, *No*, and Words of Direct Address

Exercise 111

> Commas are used after the words *yes* and *no* when they introduce sentences; to separate the words of direct address.
>
> When the name of a person addressed is the first word of a sentence, it is followed by a comma. If it is the last word of a sentence, the comma is placed before the name. If the word of address is used within the sentence, one comma is needed before the name and one after the name.

A. Add commas where needed.

1. Yes the giraffe is the tallest animal in the world.

2. Look after your brother and sister Kevin.

3. Men and women of the jury have you reached a verdict?

4. Please Alan let me look through the telescope.

5. No the whales have not reached the open seas yet.

6. Grace will you be my partner for the square dance?

7. Here's the first performance of the evening ladies and gentlemen.

8. Yuri can you read English as well as Russian?

9. Yes the largest desert is the Sahara Desert in Africa.

10. Earth students is approximately 93 million miles from the sun.

11. Penguins live in groups called rookeries Pam.

12. The male penguins Dale carry the eggs on their feet.

13. No the females do not guard the eggs.

14. Yes penguins are heavy birds.

15. This makes them good divers and swimmers Colette.

B. Complete each sentence with a noun in direct address. Use correct punctuation.

1. *Explorer I* _____ was the largest balloon ever to take flight.

2. Are you going to make popcorn while we watch the movie _____?

3. Goats _____ can graze on the steepest hills.

4. Welcome _____ to the most wonderful circus in the world.

5. _____ can you do your homework on the computer?

The Comma with Quotation Marks

Exercise 112

> Commas are used to set off short direct quotations.
>
> Place a comma after the exact words of the speaker when they come at the beginning of the sentence. Place a comma before the exact words of the speaker when they come at the end of the sentence. If the exact words of a speaker are divided, two commas are used to separate the quotation from the rest of the sentence.

A. Add commas where needed.

1. "Tom, there is something in this cave" called Amy.

2. "I'll be glad to teach you to skate" promised Danny.

3. The children shouted "Let's make a snowman!"

4. "Try another station" suggested Anne Marie.

5. "We drove through a safari park" said Henry,"and saw lions and tigers."

6. "Did you know, Francine" questioned Paul,"that the tallest building in the world is in Chicago?"

7. Sarah interrupted "Why didn't the lost explorer look at the sun?"

8. The conductor announced "Change here for Broadway!"

9. "Look" shouted Neil "at the size of its mouth!"

10. "Take the elevator to your left" directed the salesperson.

11. Lorraine called "I have your ticket for the performance."

12. The rescuers shouted "Hold on!"

13. The telephone operator said "May I help you with your call?"

14. "Do you know" asked the teacher "what crocodile tears are?"

15. "Hannah is the same name spelled forwards and backwards" laughed Hannah.

B. Complete each sentence with a speaker. Add commas where needed.

1. _____ "What a storm we are having!"

2. "An alligator " _____ "will not become your best friend."

3. "Don't forget your grandmother's birthday " _____.

4. "It's fun " _____ "to make sand castles."

5. _____ ,"A journey of a thousand miles

begins with a single step."

The Comma with Conjunctions

Exercise 113

> Commas are used before the conjunctions *and, but,* and *or* when two simple sentences are combined.

A. Add commas where needed.

1. Marie likes to use paint for her art and Georgine likes to use pastels.

2. The radio was repaired but it still doesn't work well.

3. A ram is a male sheep and a ewe is a female sheep.

4. Lobsters are delicious but they are messy to eat.

5. The guide told us to plan our day well or we may waste too much time.

B. Complete each sentence with a coordinate conjunction. Add commas where needed.

1. Fold your paper into four equal parts _____ then draw a favorite book character in each section.

2. Please don't move around in the canoe _____ you might fall into the river.

3. The sun shone brightly after the rain _____ there wasn't a rainbow.

4. A lamb is a sheep less than a year old _____ a calf is a baby cow.

5. I ran as hard and long as I could _____ I still came in last.

C. Combine each set of simple sentences with a conjunction. Add commas where needed.

1. The apples were ripe. The bananas were still a little green.

   _____

2. Don't pet the monkey. It just might bite your finger.

   _____

3. Melissa studied immediately after school. Then she went to band practice.

   _____

4. The thesaurus is a book of synonyms. The atlas is a book of maps.

   _____

Review of the Comma

Exercise 114

Add commas where needed.

1. Yes my prize lamb has fluffy wool.

2. "Don't run" cautioned the coach.

3. Mrs. Walsh inquired "In what state is the Grand Canyon?"

4. The farmer planted corn peas beans and cabbage.

5. What did you give your father for his birthday Leon?

6. Always use your seat belt Dominic.

7. Try to arrive at the airport an hour early or you may miss your flight.

8. Polly polished knives forks and spoons.

9. John may I please go along on the safari?

10. Class koalas come from Australia.

11. The teacher answered "That answer is correct."

12. Yes I have read many stories about the Civil War.

13. At Thanksgiving Americans eat turkeys chickens ducks and geese.

14. Ralph Waldo Emerson said "Hitch your wagon to a star."

15. I saw the King Tut exhibit in San Francisco and then I saw it in New York.

16. No I did not receive the package.

17. Kathy asked "Who was Coronado?"

18. In this case I carry pencils erasers a pen and a ruler.

19. Much paper is manufactured in Holyoke Massachusetts.

20. We can't see you very well but we can hear you clearly.

21. Robert Fulton class invented the steamboat.

22. Rio de Janeiro Brazil is a beautiful city in South America.

23. My brothers play tennis handball and golf.

24. "Our president is chosen every four years" said the teacher.

25. Abraham Lincoln was born on February 12 1809.

Exclamation Point; Question Mark; Apostrophe

Exercise 115

> An exclamation point is used at the end of a sentence that expresses a strong feeling; after a word or phrase that expresses a strong feeling.
>
> A question mark is used at the end of every interrogative sentence.
>
> An apostrophe is used to show ownership or possession; to mark the place where a letter or letters have been omitted.

A. Add exclamation points and question marks where needed.

1. Hurry up Mom's waiting in the car.

2. Do you like to collect buttons and badges

3. What an exciting day this is

4. That is the most magnificent house I ever saw

5. What number times three equals forty-five

6. Could you invent a flying machine

7. Be careful There is a cliff directly in front of you.

8. Are leopards and panthers the same animal

B. Add apostrophes to show possession.

1. Frans left shoe landed in a mud puddle.

2. The triplets hats were all the same color and style.

3. Could you please direct me to the mens coats?

4. What do you think happened to the horses hoof?

5. May I see the childrens menu, please?

6. The animals homes have been destroyed by the fire.

7. The thief stole the kings crown.

8. This rhinoceross skin is very thick and rough.

C. Write the contraction for each pair of words.

1. does not	_____	5. we have	_____
2. are not	_____	6. I will	_____
3. did not	_____	7. we will	_____
4. will not	_____	8. you have	_____

Direct Quotations

Exercise 116

> Quotation marks are used before and after every direct quotation. A comma is placed before or after a direct quotation. If the quotation ends with a question mark or exclamation point, the comma is not used.

A. Add quotation marks and punctuation where needed.

1. "Who was Martin Luther King?" inquired William.

2. Scott has taken his sweater replied his sister

3. Stand back shouted the guard

4. This plant is very fragile cautioned the florist

5. Uncle Pete said On Memorial Day we honor Americans who died in war

6. The teacher asked Have you ever seen a caterpillar

7. The agent announced The president will arrive in five minutes

8. The lecturer stated Edison has given the world many useful inventions

9. Stand in a straight line said the dance instructor

10. These plants should bloom in the spring remarked the gardener

11. Is the sand dollar a real animal asked Gretchen

12. Please fasten your seat belts announced Captain Mattix

13. The piano teacher questioned Can you find middle C

14. The magician whispered I will make this rabbit disappear before your very eyes

15. Cross the street at the corner cautioned the guard

B. Complete each sentence with the exact words of the speaker. Add quotation marks and punctuation where needed.

1. _____ shouted the first baseman

2. Miguel said _____

3. Eleanor asked _____

4. _____ pleaded the class

5. _____ laughed Grandpa

Divided Quotations

Exercise 117

> Quotation marks are used before and after every part of a divided quotation.

A. Add quotation marks and punctuation where needed.

1. "This is not," Paul muttered, "a very exciting game."

2. Attractive parks remarked the guide beautify a community

3. Please sobbed the little girl help me find my parents

4. The circus announced Adam will be here next week

5. What asked Jill is the biggest and most powerful musical instrument

6. Foxes yelp explained the forest ranger and wolves howl

7. Where asked Jo can I find the right answer

8. Movies about Tarzan said Bill are fascinating

9. Be careful warned Nick when you go down these steps

10. Mark Twain's real name said the writer was Samuel Clemens

11. White bread Mom remarked is the most popular bread in the world

12. Yes answered Tina Nashville is the capital of Tennessee

13. King Montezuma said the guide drank fifty cups of chocolate a day

14. Flapjacks griddle cakes hot cakes and silver dollars explained the waitress are other names for pancakes

15. There's a fire shouted the principal in the auditorium

B. Complete each sentence with the exact words of the speaker. Add quotation marks and punctuation where needed.

1. _____ Herman explained _____

2. _____ announced Alice _____

3. _____ said Roger _____

4. _____ encouraged the coach _____

5. _____ the butcher replied _____

Quotation Marks and Underlining

Exercise 118

> Quotation marks are used to enclose the titles of stories, poems, and television shows. Titles of books and works of art are printed in italics. When you write the title of a book or work of art, underline the title since you cannot write in italics.

A. Add quotation marks and underlining where needed.

1. Have you read the poem "Tug of War" by Kathleen Fraser?

2. Let's watch Teen Talent Show on television tonight.

3. The Seeing Summer is a beautiful book about a blind girl.

4. What artist painted Whistling Boy?

5. Valentine for Earth is a delightful poem by Francis Frost.

6. I enjoyed reading the short story Bowleg Bill, Cowboy of the Ocean Waves.

7. Does the library have the book Old Yeller?

8. Draw a picture after you read the poem Subways Are People.

9. The girl in the painting Girl with Watering Can looks like my little sister.

10. If I do my homework before dinner, I can watch Lovable Laughs.

11. If you want to read a funny book, try Homer Price by Robert McCloskey.

12. Read Ray Bradbury's short story The Wonderful Ice Cream Suit.

13. The painting Snap the Whip looks like the real thing.

14. You won't be able to put down the book They Lived with the Dinosaurs.

15. If you like the ocean, you'll enjoy the poem Shells by Lilian Moore.

B. Complete each sentence with appropriate information. Add quotation marks and underlining where needed.

1. _____ is my favorite book.

2. Do you like the poem _____

3. My favorite television show is _____

4. Our class went to the museum and saw the painting _____

5. In our reader we just finished the story _____

Capital Letters

Exercise 119

Capital letters are used to begin the first word in a sentence; proper nouns and proper adjectives; abbreviations when a capital letter would be used if the word were written in full; an initial; important words in titles of books, plays, poems, art objects, and compositions; the first word in a direct quotation; the first word of a line of poetry; names referring to the deity, the Bible, and other sacred books; north, south, east, and west when they refer to sections of the country; the first word in the salutation and the name of the person addressed; the first word in the complimentary close; the pronoun *I* and the interjection *O*.

A. Use the proofreading symbol (≡) to show which letters should be capitalized.

1. my sisters and i prepared christmas dinner.

2. in vermont, the hunting season began last tuesday.

3. mr. a. j. miller attended a convention in perry, oh.

4. rita recited "october's bright blue weather," a poem by helen hunt jackson.

5. "corn," said the farmer, "is our chief crop."

6. have you read the book *there's a bat in bunk five?*

7. the indians named manhattan island.

8. my mom has an authentic japanese kimono.

9. turn right on j. f. k. boulevard, then left on locust street.

10. "here we are!" exclaimed nancie. "we packed enough food to last all day."

11. i found clever poems in *a boy named mary jane and other silly verse.*

12. charles a. lindbergh flew from new york to paris.

13. i can remember being fascinated with mexican jumping beans.

14. my dear uncle raymond,

15. last summer, tom and i took a trip to kalamazoo, michigan.

B. Circle the group of words that is capitalized correctly.

1. *The Landing Of The Pilgrims*   the American flag

2. Dear aunt Mildred,   Westtown School

3. I live in the South.   Your Friend,

4. Battersby Street   Mrs. Janice p. Adrian

5. "Macavity The Mystery Cat"   Declaration of Independence

Review of Punctuation and Capitalization

Exercise 120

Add periods where needed.

1. Mr C P Reynolds began a new business

2. Nov is the abbreviation for November

3. What famous war occurred in A D 1066?

4. Dr Horn arrived at the hospital at 3:55 A M

5. Workers at the Pennsboro Electric Co went on strike today

Write the correct abbreviation for each word.

6. Tuesday _____

7. liter _____

8. Captain _____

9. pint _____

10. Mister _____

Add commas where needed.

11. Our first three presidents were Washington Adams and Jefferson.

12. On September 19 1796 Washington delivered his famous farewell address.

13. "Do not count your chickens before they are hatched" said Aesop.

14. Yes the Mediterranean Sea is the saltiest sea.

15. Do you know Carmen what the name Los Angeles means?

16. "Let's enter the hot dog eating contest" suggested Irene.

17. "Okay" said Buddy "but I just had two pieces of pizza."

18. A ballet is a story danced to music and an opera is a story that is sung and acted.

19. Pauline visit the Seashore Trolley Museum in Kennebunkport Maine.

20. Mickey wanted to enter the race but his bike had a flat tire.

Review of Capitalization and Punctuation

Exercise 120, continued.

Add exclamation points, question marks, and apostrophes where needed.

21. Hurrah The storm is over.

22. How much damage did it do

23. Im going to help our neighbors.

24. My friends house has a lot of damage.

25. What a terrible twenty minutes that was

Add quotation marks where needed.

26. Can you design a new cover for this magazine? asked the editor.

27. I can, said Larry, but I'll need large paper and pastels.

28. Try, mentioned the editor, to draw some children working in the classroom.

29. Larry questioned, Should they be first graders or sixth graders?

30. Let's make them third graders, suggested Ms. Eliot.

Add quotation marks or underlining where needed.

31. On page 12, Sara, you'll find the poem The Dentist.

32. Look for the novel Anna to the Infinite Power on the third shelf.

33. Carefully study the face of the young girl in the painting Mona Lisa.

34. The book Bridge to Terabithia won the Newbery Award.

35. Please, can I be the troll in the poem Perry-the-Winkle?

Use the proofreading symbol (≡) to show which letters should be capitalized.

36. Chris loves to read Elinor Wylie's poem "velvet shoes."

37. Some of the oldest streets in america are in the east.

38. Mr. Holland asked, "can you punctuate this sentence correctly?"

39. dear mrs. potter,

40. p.s. is an interesting character in the story "so much unfairness of things."

Homophones

Exercise 121

Homophones are words that sound alike, but differ in meaning and in spelling. For example, *sent*, *cent*, and *scent* are homophones.

Write on each line the correct word from the group of homophones.

herd	ceiling	piece	fir	creek
heard	sealing	peace	fur	creak
capital	led	weigh	beech	altar
capitol	lead	way	beach	alter

1. Have you ever _____ that story?

   The _____ of cattle is on its way to market.

2. The _____ of the envelopes was done by machine.

   The _____ of the room is painted white.

3. The _____ of cake was delicious.

   Let us all hope for _____ .

4. Have you ever read the tale of the _____ tree?

   That _____ coat is very expensive.

5. Did you hear the boards _____ ?

   We sat under a tree by the _____ .

6. The class visited Washington, D.C., our nation's _____ .

   Congress meets in the _____ building.

7. He _____ the troops to victory.

   _____ is a heavy metallic element.

8. _____ that package on the desk.

   The _____ through the forest is beautiful but long.

9. The _____ tree shed its leaves early this fall.

   Hundreds of shells were lying on the _____ .

10. We will _____ our plans if it begins to rain.

    A gold cloth covered the stone _____ .

Antonyms

Exercise 122

> Antonyms are words that are opposite in meaning. For example, *softly* and *loudly* are antonyms.

A. Underline the two words that are opposite in meaning.

1. His former enemy became his best friend.

2. Mr. Smith raised his disciplined voice and calmed the unruly crowd.

3. The innocent sometimes suffer for the guilty.

4. Roses are scarce in winter, but they are plentiful in summer.

5. I saw two industrious ants, and one lazy one.

6. The ugly duckling became a beautiful swan.

7. The elevator ascended to the sixth floor, then descended to the basement.

8. The girls ran quickly, but the boys walked slowly.

9. Everybody admires a courteous person, but not a rude one.

10. A cloudy day is dull, while a sunny one is bright.

B. Complete each sentence with an antonym of the italicized word.

1. Monica has been *present* four days and _____ one day.

2. *Cold* drinks are refreshing in _____ weather.

3. Rise *early*, and you will not be _____ for the trip.

4. Cotton is a leading *export* of the United States, while coffee is a major _____ .

5. *Above* the bridge soared an airplane, while _____ the bridge glided a pleasure boat.

6. This box is *empty*, but that one is _____ .

7. A *narrow* lane led to the _____ highway.

8. This bread is *fresh*, but that is _____ .

9. The instructor *asked* the question and Michael _____ . it promptly.

10. The hare moved *quickly*, but the turtle crawled along _____ .

Synonyms

Exercise 123

> Synonyms are words that have the same general meaning. For example, *guard*, *defend*, and *protect* are synonyms.

A. Below each sentence, cross out the word that is not a synonym of the italicized word.

1. Aladdin traveled with his *friends*.

    companions   enemies   comrades   associates

2. The rider immediately realized his *peril*.

    danger   risk   mistake   hazard

3. *Glistening* coins made up his valuable collection.

    bright   sparkling   glittering   rare

4. Our journey may prove *tedious*.

    profitable   irksome   tiresome   wearisome

5. King Midas was a *foolish* man.

    unwise   rash   sensible   stupid

6. Andrew *answered* without hesitation.

    replied   responded   retorted   spoke

7. Our parents try to *protect* us from danger.

    defend   remove   safeguard   shield

8. John Bannister Tabb was always a *happy* lad.

    jolly   cheerful   joyous   generous

9. A loud cry *frightened* the animal.

    awakened   terrified   alarmed   startled

10. The judge showed *mercy* toward the prisoner.

    compassion   clemency   cruelty   pity

11. Doug told the audience a funny story.

    unhappy   amusing   witty   comical

Recognizing the Exact Meaning of Words

Exercise 124

> While synonyms have the same general meaning, there is often a slight difference which makes one word better in a sentence than another.

A. Complete each sentence with the best word from the group of synonyms.

dark	**dismal**	**dim**

1. A _____ light burned in the distance.

2. Dampness and lack of light made the dungeon very _____ .

think	**imagine**	**believe**

3. We _____ that the earth is round.

4. _____ clearly, students.

sing	**chant**	**chirp**

5. Did the choir _____ the ancient hymn?

6. All winter long, the sparrows _____ in our yard.

group	**crowd**	**company**

7. A large_____ attended the Super Bowl.

8. Each reading class consists of a small _____ of students.

afraid	**alarmed**	**cautious**

9. The guide took a _____ step forward.

10. Helen is_____ of lightning.

tell	**announce**	**proclaim**

11. Tomorrow he will _____ the name of the winner.

12. Can you_____ me the correct answer?

put	**place**	**deposit**

13. Does your father_____ his money in this bank?

14. _____ this bowl of flowers in the middle of the table.

catch	**seize**	**grasp**

15. Invaders will _____ the city and will take many prisoners.

16. My brother can _____ a ball with either hand.

Using Action Verbs

Exercise 125

| Writing can be improved by using verbs that describe actions clearly and vividy. |

These verbs may be used in place of *went.*

strolled	scurried	galloped	glided
curled	trotted	swerved	marched
bounded	tiptoed	hobbled	hopped

A. Complete each sentence with a synonym for *went.*

1. The band _____ down State Street.

2. A crippled boy _____ across the road.

3. The boys _____ into the deserted house.

4. The tired horse _____ along the dusty road.

5. The alley cat_____ after the mouse.

6. The driver _____ suddenly to the right.

7. The young couple _____ through the park.

8. Around the track _____ the horse.

9. Smoke _____ out of the chimney.

10. Our boat_____ downstream.

11. The excited boy_____ into the room.

12. A small rabbit _____ right up to me.

B. Complete each sentence with a synonym for *rang.*

| chimed | tolled | tinkled |
| jingled | pealed | clanged |

1. The bell _____ in the light wind.

2. Sleigh bells_____merrily.

3. The clock _____the hour.

4. The bell _____for the funeral.

5. Wedding bells _____ through the church.

6. The bell on the ocean buoy _____ through the night.

Using Colorful Adjectives

Exercise 126

| Writing can be improved by substituting colorful adjectives for dull, colorless ones. |

Good is an overworked adjective. These words may be used to paint more vivid pictures.

interesting   excellent   enjoyable
correct   resourceful   intelligent

A. Complete each sentence with a synonym for *good.*

1. We spent an _____ day at the picnic.

2. Loretta does _____ work.

3. Molly uses _____ English.

4. Elizabeth gave an _____ answer.

5. This is an _____ book.

6. The president of the company is a _____ man.

B. Complete each sentence with a synonym for *big.*

tall   huge   enormous
towering   immense   vast

1. Modern architects erect _____ buildings.

2. The man became heir to a _____ estate.

3. A _____ elephant led the parade.

4. In the park stood an _____ statue of Napoleon.

5. My uncle is a _____ man.

6. The wind has carved that _____ rock into fantastic shapes.

C. Complete each sentence with a synonym for *pretty.*

beautiful   dainty   becoming
attractive   picturesque   delicate

1. She wore a _____ hat to the wedding.

2. Before the statue stood a vase of _____ flowers.

3. Ruth described the _____ scene to her friends.

4. A _____ sunset inspired me to write that poem.

5. The decorations in our classroom are very _____ .

6. At the windows of the cottage hung _____ lace curtains.

Rewriting Rambling Sentences

Exercise 127

> Too many long sentences, strung together with *and,* make writing dull and uninteresting. Revise such sentences by dividing them into shorter sentences.

Rewrite each sentence into shorter, more concise sentences.

1. Louisville is a large tobacco market and Lexington is a large tobacco market, too, and many cigars and cigarettes are manufactured in these cities.

   _____

   _____

2. Yesterday I read the life of Martin Luther King, Jr. and I enjoyed the book very much.

   _____

   _____

3. The children built a snowman and they placed a pipe in his mouth and a hat on his head.

   _____

   _____

4. John is going fishing this afternoon and he's my friend and I would like to go with him.

   _____

   _____

5. Mr. Jackson became governor and he governed wisely and he was very good to the people.

   _____

   _____

6. Susan is a pretty little girl and her blond hair is curly and her blue eyes are bright.

   _____

   _____

Letter Writing

Exercise 128

A friendly letter has five parts: the heading, which contains the address of the writer and the date of the letter; the salutation, or greeting; the body, which contains the message; the complimentary close, or farewell; the signature, or name of the writer.

A. Use the proofreading symbol (≡) to indicate which letters should be capitalized. Add punctuation where needed.

1754 peachtree street

atlanta ga 30309

june 11 19__

dear patricia

B. Add punctuation where needed to the letter. Use the proofreading symbol (≡) to indicate capitalization.

217 parker avenue

new london ct 06051

november 18 19__

dear grandmom

thanksgiving is almost here and i can hardly wait to visit you mother asked me to tell you that we will arrive the day before maybe granddad will meet us at the corner

already i have visions of delicious turkey and pumpkin pies remind uncle adam that he promised to take us to the football game in the afternoon

i like school very much this year you will be proud of me when i show you my papers i'll bring my report card with me

your grandson

tod

Letter Writing

Exercise 129

In thank-you letters, the gift and the reason you like the gift should be mentioned.

In the following letter, all the parts run together. Copy the letter with each part in its proper place. Add capital letters and punctuation where needed.

315 south seventh street milwaukee wisconsin 53233 june 2 19__ dear uncle john how did you know that i wanted a skateboard for my birthday now i can really practice for the tournament you couldn't have given me a better gift thank you very much your grateful nephew benny

_____

_____

_____

_____

_____

_____

_____

_____

_____

_____

_____

_____

_____

Handbook of Terms

Nouns

A **noun** is a name word. A noun may name a person, a place, or a thing.
There are two main kinds of nouns: proper nouns and common nouns.
 A **proper noun** names a particular person, place, or thing.
 A **common noun** names any one of a class of persons, places, or things.
A noun has **number**, **gender**, and **case**. These are called the qualities of a noun.
Number tells about one person or thing (singular number) or more than one
 (plural number).
 A **singular noun** tells about one person, place, or thing.
 A **plural noun** tells about more than one person, place, or thing. Most plural
 nouns end in s.
Gender is that quality of a noun by which sex is indicated.
 The **masculine gender** indicates males.
 The **feminine gender** indicates females.
 The **neuter gender** indicates objects and places.
 Some nouns may be either masculine or feminine.
Case of a noun shows its relation to other words in the sentence.
 A noun used as the **subject** in a sentence is in the **nominative case**.
 The person, the place, or the thing talked about in the sentence is the subject.
 A noun used as a **subjective complement** is in the **nominative case**.
 A subjective complement completes the meaning of a linking verb and names the
 same person, place, or thing as the subject.
 A noun used in **direct address** is in the **nominative case**.
 A noun of address names the person spoken to. A noun of address is set off from
 the rest of the sentence by a comma or commas.
 A noun used as the **object** in a sentence is in the **objective case**.
 The person, place, or thing that is the receiver of the action is the direct object.
 A noun used as the **object of a preposition** is in the **objective case**. The noun
 that follows the preposition in a prepositional phrase is called the object of a
 preposition.
The **possessive form** of a noun expresses possession or ownership.
 To form the singular possessive, add 's to the singular form of the noun.
 To form the plural possessive of nouns that end in s, add the apostrophe only.
 If the plural form of a noun does not end in s, add 's.

Pronouns

A **pronoun** takes the place of a noun.

A **personal pronoun** shows by its form
 the speaker (first person) I, mine, me, we, ours, us.
 the person spoken to (second person) you, yours.
 the person spoken about (third person) he, she, it, his, hers, its, him, her, they,
 theirs, them.

A singular pronoun takes the place of a singular noun; a plural pronoun takes
 the place of a plural noun.

The **singular pronouns** are *I, me, he, she, it, him, her.*
The **plural pronouns** are *we, us, you, they, them.*

A pronoun that refers to males is **masculine gender**; a pronoun that refers to females is **feminine gender**; a pronoun that refers to an object is **neuter gender**.

Compound personal pronouns are formed by adding -self or -*selves* to certain forms of the personal pronouns.

The compound personal pronouns of the **first person** are *myself* and *ourselves*.

The compound personal pronouns of the **second person** are *yourself* and *yourselves*.

The compound personal pronouns of the **third person** are *himself, herself, itself,* and *themselves*.

A compound personal pronoun must agree with its antecedent in person, number, and gender.

A pronoun used as the subject of a verb is in the **nominative case.**
A pronoun used as a subjective complement is in the **nominative case.**
A pronoun used as the direct object of a verb is in the **objective case.**
A pronoun used as the object of a preposition is in the **objective case.**

Possessive pronouns show possession or ownership by the speaker, the person spoken to, or the person or thing spoken about.

The personal pronouns are used with auxiliary verbs to form contractions.

A contraction is one word made from two words. The apostrophe (') is used to show the omission of a letter or letters.

Possessives express ownership or possession. This form of the word does not take an apostrophe.

Possessives: its, your, their
Contractions: *it's, you're, they're*

Adjectives

An adjective describes or limits a noun or pronoun.

A **descriptive adjective** describes a noun or a pronoun.

A descriptive adjective formed from a proper noun is a **proper adjective.**

A descriptive adjective not formed from a proper noun is a **common adjective.**

A **limiting adjective** either points out an object or indicates number. The limiting adjectives may be divided into (1) articles, (2) numeral adjectives, (3) demonstrative adjectives, and (4) possessive adjectives.

The articles are the, an, and a.

A **numeral adjective** indicates exact number, as in *ten* or *third.*

Some adjectives tell about number: *many, few, several some.*

A **demonstrative adjective** points out a definite person, place, or thing.

The demonstrative adjectives agree in number with the nouns they modify.

This and *these* denote objects that are near.

That and *those* denote distant objects.

A **possessive adjective** denotes ownership. The possessive adjectives are *my, his, her, its, our, your, their.*

Possessive adjectives are often confused with contractions that sound like them.

Possessive adjectives express ownership or possession.

An **interrogative adjective** is used in asking a question.

The usual position of the adjective is before the noun.

Some adjectives follow and complete the meaning of a linking verb. These are called **subjective complements.** The adjective that follows a linking verb describes or limits the subject.

Comparison is the change which adjectives undergo to express different degrees of quality, quantity, or value.

The **positive degree** expresses a quality about one person or thing.

The **comparative degree** compares two persons or things.

The **superlative degree** compares three or more persons or things.

To form the comparative degree of most adjectives, add the suffix *-er.* For some adjectives of two or more syllables, add *more* before the adjective.

To form the superlative degree of most adjectives, add the suffix *-est.* For some adjectives of two or more syllables, add *most* before the adjective.

The comparative *fewer* refers to number; *less* refers to quantity.

Some words may function as nouns or adjectives.

A noun is a name word; an adjective describes or limits a noun.

Verbs

A **verb** is a word that expresses action or being.

A verb phrase is a group of words used to do the work of a single verb.

A verb used with another verb is called an auxiliary verb.

A regular verb forms its past and its past participle by adding *-d* or *-ed* to the present.

An **irregular verb** does not form its past and its past participle by adding *-d* or *-ed* to the present.

A **transitive verb** expresses an action that passes from a doer to a receiver.

An **intransitive verb** has no receiver of its action.

Some verbs may be considered transitive or intransitive, according to their use in the sentence.

A **linking verb** links the subject with a noun, a pronoun, or an adjective.

The word or group of words that completes the meaning of a linking verb is called a subjective complement. The subjective complement may be a noun, a pronoun, or an adjective.

The verb *be* in its various forms—*am, is, are, was, were, will be, have been,* and so forth—is the most common linking verb.

Linking verbs are not action verbs.

Tense indicates the time of the action or the being.

Present tense shows action that is happening now or that happens again and again.

Past tense shows action that has happened.

Future tense shows action that will happen.

The verb must always agree with its subject.

A singular subject requires a singular verb.

A plural subject requires a plural verb.

A singular verb ends in *s* or *es* in the present tense.

A plural verb does not end in *s* or *es* in the present tense.

Use *is* and *was* when the subject is singular. Use *are* and *were* when the subject is plural.

Use *am* with the pronoun *I.* Use *doesn't* with singular nouns and the pronouns *he, she,* and *it.*

Use *don't* with plural nouns and the pronouns *I, we, you, they.*

The verb *lie (lie, lay, lain)* means to rest or to recline. It is always intransitive.
The verb *lay (lay, laid, laid)* means to put or place in position. It is always transitive.
The verb *sit (sit, sat, sat)* means to have or keep a seat. It is always intransitive.
The verb *set (set, set, set)* means to place or to fix. It is always transitive.
The verb *teach (teach, taught, taught)* means to give instruction.
The verb *learn (learn, learned, learned)* means to receive instruction.
The verb *let (let, let, let)* means to permit or to allow.
The verb *leave (leave, left, left)* means to depart or abandon.

Adverbs

An **adverb** modifies a verb, an adjective, or another adverb.
  Adverbs of time answer the questions *when* or *how often.*
  Adverbs of place answer the question *where.*
  Adverbs of manner answer the questions *how* or *in what manner.*

Adverbs have three degrees of comparison.
  Some adverbs form the comparative degree by adding *-er* to the positive degree.
  Some adverbs form the superlative degree by adding *-est* to the positive degree.
  Many adverbs form the comparative degree by using the word *more* or *less* before the positive degree of the adverb.
  Many adverbs form the superlative by using the word *most* or *least* before the positive degree.
  Some adverbs are compared irregularly.

If a sentence has one negative adverb such as *not,* avoid using another negative word, such as *no* or *never.*

Prepositions and Phrases

A **preposition** is a word placed before a noun or a pronoun. The noun or pronoun is called the object of the preposition.

A phrase is a group of related words used as a single part of speech. Since this group of words is introduced by a preposition, it is called a prepositional phrase.

Phrases consist of a preposition and an object.
  An adjectival phrase is used as an adjective and modifies a noun.
  An adverbial phrase is used as an adverb and modifies a verb
  Between is used in speaking of two persons or things; *among* is used in speaking of more than two.
  From is used in speaking of a person from whom something is received. *Off* means *away from.* The expression *off of* is never correct.

Conjunctions

A conjunction is a word used to connect words or groups of words.
Coordinate conjunctions connect subjects, predicates, direct objects, and sentences.

Interjections

An interjection expresses some strong and sudden emotion—delight, disgust, pain, assent, joy, impatience, surprise, sorrow, nonsense, wonder.

Sentences

A sentence is a group of words expressing a complete thought.

A declarative sentence states a fact. It is followed by a period.

An **interrogative sentence** asks a question. It is followed by a question mark.

An **imperative sentence** expresses a command. It is followed by a period.

An **exclamatory sentence** expresses strong or sudden emotion. It is followed by an exclamation point.

The **subject** names a person, a place, or a thing about which a statement is made.

The **predicate** tells something about the subject.

The subject with all its modifiers is called the **complete subject.**

The predicate with all its modifiers, objects, and complements is called the **complete predicate.**

Whenever the complete predicate follows the complete subject, a sentence is in the **natural order.**

Whenever the complete predicate or part of the predicate comes before the subject, a sentence is in the **inverted order.**

Natural order is generally preferred.

A **simple sentence** contains one subject and one predicate. Either or both may be compound.

If the subject in a sentence consists of more than one noun or pronoun, it is said to be a **compound subject.**

If the predicate consists of more than one verb, it is said to be a **compound predicate.**

If one direct object has more than one noun or pronoun, it is said to be a **compound object.**

Punctuation

A **period** is used at the end of a declarative or an imperative sentence; after an abbreviation or an initial.

Commas are used to separate words or groups of words in a series; to set off parts of dates, addresses, or geographical names; to set off words in direct address; after the words *yes* and *no* when they introduce sentences; to set off short direct quotations, unless an question mark or exclamation point is required; to separate simple sentences connected by the conjunctions *and, but,* and *or*; after the salutation and complimentary close in a social letter.

An **exclamation point** is used after an exclamatory sentence; after an exclamatory word or phrase.

An **question mark** is used at the end of a question.

Quotation marks are used before and after every direct quotation and every part of a divided quotation; to enclose titles of short stories, poems, magazine articles, television shows, and radio programs.

Titles of books, magazines, newspapers, movies, and works of art are usually printed in italics or underlined.

An **apostrophe** is used to show possession; to indicate the omission of a letter or letters in a word.

Capital letters are used for the first word in a sentence; for the first word of a direct quotation; for proper nouns; for the directions north, east, south, and west when they refer to a section of a country or of the world; for the principal words in the titles of books, plays, poems, and pictures; for the pronoun *I* and the interjection *O*; for names referring to the deity, Bible, and other sacred books; for two-letter state abbreviations; for abbreviations when capitals would be used if the words were written in full; for the first word and the name of a person addressed in the salutation of a letter; for the first word in the complimentary close of a lettter.

Forms for Parsing

A Noun, Pronoun, and Verb

To ensure maintenance of work already taught and to provide opportunity for greater understanding, students should be taught a form for parsing nouns, pronouns, and verbs.

The forms below may be printed on charts for classroom use. It is suggested that, in the beginning, students be permitted to use guides in parentheses. When students become more familiar with the form and can respond with fluency, these guides can be eliminated.

Parsing the Noun or Pronoun

_____ is a *(common—proper)* noun
          (singular—plural) number
          (first—second—third) person
          (masculine—feminine—neuter) gender
        * *(nominative—possessive—objective)* case
          because *(give appropriate use)*

*Nominative Case
subject of predicate
subjective complement
address

*Possessive Case
ownership
(nouns usually
use *'s* or *s'* ;
pronouns: *mine,
ours, yours, his,
hers, its, theirs*)

*Objective Case
direct object
object of preposition

Parsing the Verb

_____ is *(regular/irregular)* form
          (transitive/intransitive/linking) use
          (simple) tense
          (singular/plural) number

Diagram Analysis

The diagram is a visual outline of the sentence. Its purpose is to show the essentials of the sentence (*subject* and *predicate*) and the relationship of all other words and constructions to these essentials.

The **main diagram line** is the focal point of the diagram. It is a horizontal line.

_____

This line should be carefully drawn with a ruler both on paper and at the chalkboard. The length of the line will be determined by the length of the words to be placed on it.

Steps in Diagraming a Simple Sentence

The form of the sentence (simple, compound, complex) determines the number of main diagram lines that will be used.

Simple Sentence   Compound and Complex Sentences

_____   _____

                                   _____

                        (Each clause has its
                          own line.)

| In the spring, many beautiful birds sing happily in our garden. |

1. This sentence is simple because it has one subject and one predicate and expresses one thought. Therefore we begin the diagram with the **main diagram line.**

_____

2. The **predicate** is *sing.* Place *sing* on the center of the line.

sing
_____

3. *Who* sing? *What* sing? *Birds* sing. The **subject** is *birds.* Place *birds* before the predicate and separate with a vertical line that cuts through the main diagram line.

birds | sing

4. Birds sing *whom*? No answer. Birds sing *what*? No answer. There is no **direct object.** (If there were a direct object, it would follow the predicate and would be separated from the predicate by a vertical line above the main diagram.)

birds | sing |

5. To find the **predicate modifiers,** ask the questions *how, when, where, why.* Sing *how?* Sing *happily.* Sing *when?* Sing *in the spring.* Sing *where?* Sing *in our garden.* These predicate modifiers are placed below the predicate on slanted lines, each modifier on its own line. Prepositional phrases serving as **adverbial modifiers** are diagramed as shown.

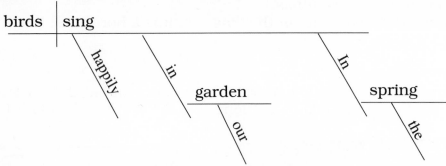

6. To find the **subject modifiers,** ask the questions *what, what kind, how many, whose.* *What* birds? No answer. *What kind* of birds? *Beautiful* birds. *How many* birds? *Many* birds. *Whose* birds? No answer.

   Subject modifiers are *many* and *beautiful.* These modifiers are placed on slanted lines below the subject. If there were **adjectival phrases,** they would be placed on the phrase bracket similar to the one used for the adverbial phrases in Step 5.

7. To find **object modifiers,** use the same procedures as outlined for subject modifiers in Step 6.
   The completed diagram would be

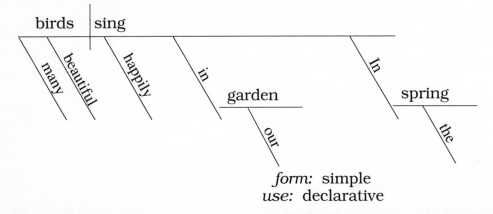

   form: simple
   use: declarative

N.B. Examples of all types of diagrams are provided in *Voyages in English* in both teacher's manual and student book. Students should be aware of the meaning of each line and should be taught to use these lines accurately.
   The basic sentence patterns are as follows:

(a) subject | predicate

(b) subject | predicate | direct object

(c) subject | predicate \ subjective complement
              (action verb)   (noun, pronoun, adjective)
              (verb of being)

Compound subjects

They | played | ball.

Tom ‾|‾⟍
    |and⟩| played | ball
Fred _|_⟋

Point out the need to write the subject in such a way as to provide a sense of equality between each name.

Subjects always appear on horizontal lines

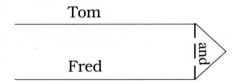

        Tom
——————————————
        Fred

The **coordinate conjunction** is placed on a broken line between the words it joins.

      Tom

      Fred

Subjects are joined by solid lines to the main diagram line.

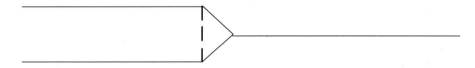

Compound predicates

The same directions apply here: a single horizontal line for each predicate. The conjunction is placed on a broken line joining the predicates.

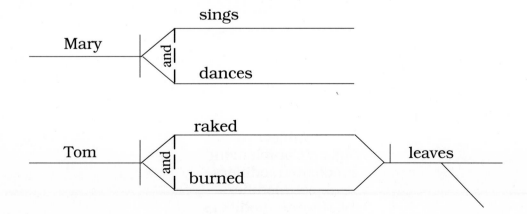

             sings
Mary
             dances

             raked
Tom   leaves
             burned

Sentence Analysis

Sentence analysis is a classroom-tested strategy designed to aid students in mastering the study of the sentence through the study of its grammatical components and their relationships to one another.

Sentence analysis begins with a consideration of the *whole*—a careful and thoughtful reading of the sentence—to determine the thought expressed and the manner in which that thought is written. Having determined its *form* and *use*, the students proceed to examine the main idea, beginning with the predicate and the subject. From here, students identify the details, the modifiers in the sentence.

Sentence analysis is an oral drill in which each student responds to one point in some predetermined order; by row, by group, or by number. The responses move at a fairly fast pace to hold interest. The drill should last approximately five minutes at the beginning of the grammar period several times a week. Prolonging it can make it a chore rather than a challenge.

The sentence analysis chart (see below) is placed where it can be seen by all students. The sentence to be analyzed can be selected from the textbook or workbook and is written on the chalkboard.

All students participate in the drill. Ideally, the teacher should be an observer during this time, allowing the students to perform the drill without assistance. From student performance, the teacher can evaluate the students' mastery of grammar and can identify those areas that need review.

At first, students will require a gradual introduction to the sentence analysis until they understand the form and develop the skills for using it.

A gradual, consistent drill in the use of grammatical concepts is a good way to understand how the English language is structured and why these patterns are used to express thought.

CHART

SENTENCE ANALYSIS

Sentence
Form
Use
Predicate
Subject
Object/Complement
Predicate modifiers
Subject modifiers
Obj./Comp. modifiers
Parts of speech

A chart similar to the above can easily be prepared on cardboard, approximately 22" x 14". The chart is used as a visual aid to guide students through the steps of sentence analysis.